the town called potential

the town called potential

a story about living
outside the box

JACK VANDERMERE

CHRISTIAN ART
PUBLISHERS

Published in South Africa by CHRISTIAN ART PUBLISHERS
PO Box 1599, Vereeniging, 1930

© 2005
First edition 2005

Cover designed by Christian Art Publishers

Set in 11 on 15pt Palatino by Christian Art Publishers

Printed and bound by Paarl Print, Paarl, South Africa

ISBN 1-86920-524-3

05 06 07 08 09 10 11 12 13 14 – 11 10 9 8 7 6 5 4 3 2

Dedicated to ...

all dreamers, everywhere
all pilgrims who see beyond horizons
all lovers of life
all souls in whom burns the eternal flame.

Table of Contents

Foreword

THE STORY OF an ancient gray town came to me when well-known artist and friend of mine, Barry de Villiers, asked me to address his guests at the opening of an art exhibition. Seeing the mastery of his work and the beauty of the colors made me think of the secret of excellence. What is it that gives great artists that ability to enchant us with beauty?

No doubt, we lesser mortals will in vain attempt to be a Beethoven, Van Gogh or Shakespeare. And yet, there is something that we can learn from all the great artists. None of them reached the heights they did without dedication, their talents alone could not make them reach their potential.

All of us cannot become, but then, all of us were not destined to become great artists or leaders. Yet, each one of us can aim at and reach the unique target set for us, and, in a sense, we will all have to pay the same price to do so. This simple story speaks of that price.

Somehow, when writing this story, I felt that I was on a journey, an adventure, not of creating something, but of discovering, almost listening in. I found an ancient town where people reminded me so much of myself. I discovered secrets and learned about dragons and riddles. And this ancient world taught me more about my own world.

My humble hope is that these words will enter minds and hearts, take them on a journey to ancient worlds of wisdom and then back to their own world with new hope, joy and resolve.

Chapter 1

OF STORIES AND BEAUTY

And the disciples came, and said unto him, Why speakest thou unto them in parables? He answered and said unto them, because it is given unto you to know the mysteries of the kingdom of heaven, but to them it is not given.

MATTHEW 13:10-11

THE GREATEST TEACHER who ever lived was a storyteller. He gave two reasons for using stories to teach people about life: hiding the truth and opening up the truth.

When Jesus spoke, some understood life better and others had no idea what He was talking about. The difference was in how they approached life.

There were those who were set in their ways. Their own tradition and ideas were the only wisdom that made sense to them. Their own everyday lives of security and safety. No time for anything beyond their own minute idea of reality.

Jesus likened their hearts to stone. Their eyes were closed to the beauty of mystery. Their world was small. Nothing outside their comfortable understanding of the black-and-whiteness of their rules for life was acceptable to them.

The Great Teacher challenged them to a life beyond the gray living of black and white certainties. There is a world of color out there, a world where our lives can become works of art. Nothing is set and certain in the world Jesus painted with His stories.

Some venture out into that great mysterious world and become artists of life. They join the great story, they become characters in the drama of eternity.

Others remain in their small disappearing worlds.

They choose not to be part of the story of the Great Storyteller and eventually disappear from its pages.

And so we have to ask ourselves if we are ready to venture out into the real world of eternal beauty. Will we allow ourselves to become artists of life?

In the ancient world we are about to join, there is a voice of wisdom speaking. The hero of our story was an artist of life. If you will be silent and turn these pages you will see the strategies of the enemies of all artists of life. In this, our first encounter with the people from The Town called Potential, let us pause and ponder on the meaning of these pages.

In the doings of our hero and his family we will discover some of the secrets of all artists of life. One such secret is the infatuation with the opportunities life has to offer. They were not afraid of the threat of the unknown.

You will note how new things were to them the energy that drove them on to the discovery of tomorrow. Maybe there are hidden inside your soul some dreams of new things.

Fear comes with these dreams, but to turn around and let go of your dreams will be to allow fear to steal from you the colors that the Great Artist wishes to add to the artwork of your life. And then maybe you will remember the words of Jesus:

And Jesus said unto him, no man, having put his hand to the plough, and looking back, is fit for the kingdom of God.

LUKE 9:62

Witness also that The Brave One we will meet in our story, refused to let conformity rule his life. A wise man once said that courage is not simply a virtue, but the very substance of every virtue when it is tested.

Mercy or honesty or chastity needs to be strengthened by courage or else it will yield to danger. And conditional mercy or honesty or chastity becomes masked cruelty, deceit or unchastity.

We would be wise to note from history how many tragedies have resulted from the decisions of the majority. We will find many a great man and woman in the small company of the minority. So too will you find our hero.

Creating an artwork out of your life often means having the courage to say goodbye to the crowds of popularity. It may mean that you will be the only person shouting when the majority is silent, or the only one questioning the decisions and opinions of those who rule in the chambers of conformity.

To always please people is to fear them. You will remember that centuries ago some fool, in trying to please the multitude, saved the criminal and crucified the King:

And so Pilate, willing to content the people, released Barab-bas unto them, and delivered Jesus, when he had scourged him, to be crucified.

MARK 15:15

Notice, finally, the flame of passion burning in the heart of our hero. Each of us has to look inward and often test the waters of the soul. These streams run wildly in the artists of life. No hush-hush living will do for them. No lukewarm hoping things will turn out all right.

These ancient pages are aflame with passion. We find here a man who could not wait passively for life to merely happen and we are reminded of the kind of man Jesus spoke of:

From the days of John the Baptist until now, the kingdom of heaven has been forcefully advancing, and forceful men lay hold of it.

MATTHEW 11:12 (NIV)

an artist of life

IN ANCIENT TIMES there was a town, The Town called Potential. Students of the ancient books of wisdom say that The Town called Potential was not only a very old town, but it was in fact the oldest of all towns, in the oldest of all countries.

The Town called Potential was nestled at the foot of a mountain in a country called Humanity which had more citizens than any other country in the world.

However, rumor had it that, sadly, another country called Dreamless, where one could find the cities Majority,

Security, Tragedy, and The Great Desert Despair, was growing mysteriously faster than Humanity.

In The Town called Potential, in the country Humanity, lived people that one could best describe as being almost wonderful, vaguely beautiful, very nearly ingenious and definitely (although not really aware of it) very precious.

They had rather unusual names, names like Aldore. The name Aldore is in itself a very beautiful name and in that ancient language it spoke of great things, but these people were very uncomfortable with the meaning of their names. One could say that the meaning of their names was disturbing to them.

They were very apprehensive at the thought of greatness. Greatness spoke of challenges and courage, and challenges and courage spoke of unknown dangers. This left them with an awkward problem, since they were also very uncomfortable with the idea of giving their newborn children new names. New names were so ... well, so *new*. And they felt very uncomfortable at the thought of creating any new things.

They solved their problem by keeping their old names which spoke of great things, but they added to and took away from every beautiful name something to make it sound more mundane. So, Aldore was called Plain old Al. In the same way, Olmardena preferred being called

Good old Olma. In fact, everyone in town was Plain old this; Good old that; or just Old this or that. Asterbrontt was Good old Bronty; Delgralina was Plain old Delli; Gomerthall was Old Gomy; Brendorkann was old Brendy; Gwandelinta was old Gwandy, and so on.

Because they avoided to ever use their proper names, or ever think of what the names meant, it happened over decades and centuries that the meaning of these names was forgotten completely.

Even so, through the ages such a complete sentiment of disassociation had arisen with one of these names that it was absolutely never used at all. It was decided that all those who, because of their lineage, were to receive this name would not be named at all. They would only be called after their occupation or some peculiar trait or characteristic.

The hero of our story was one such heir of the dreaded name, and was simply called The Strange One or The Owner of the House of Many Colors – for reasons which soon will become obvious.

These people with the awkward names had another rather awkward habit. They lived in identical square houses. The houses were all painted gray – not a dark and boldly aggressive gray, nor a light and decoratively brighter gray, but a very neutral and a very proper gray.

Every year, on a certain day, all the people of The Town called Potential repainted their exactly identical square houses the exactly identical neutral color gray. This was the way they had always done it.

The reason for painting all the houses on the same day every year was that it was the only way these people could make sure that their houses were always exactly the same color.

This was very important to them, the reason being that there was a family in The Town called Potential who decided to be different and paint their house the brightest and most beautiful colors one could imagine. They even went as far as adding rooms to their house and changing its shape. They planted a beautiful flower garden. This was unheard of since no other family in town had any gardens except fruit and vegetable gardens.

When asked why they did the strange thing of expanding their house, they simply said that they had no choice, that their dreams were too big for the smallness of the little gray houses.

And could they dream! During those long summer evenings, having watched the beauty of their ancient sunsets, they would dream the kind of dreams that made them feel that all of life was one great invitation to discover the ancient beauty of the past and join the mysterious and promising beauty of the future.

They dreamed of worlds beyond their gray old town. They dreamed of palaces, brave warriors and a kind of life where beauty and wisdom stabbed constantly into the heart, beckoning it to new frontiers.

The rest of the townsfolk were terrified and appalled by these dreams that obviously could bring great discomfort and danger in real life. They also thought that it was very extravagant and improper to have a house of many colors (which was not even square in shape!) with a garden of many colors.

So, as was the case with all important matters, the town council immediately summoned a special meeting in the big, square, gray town hall.

After discussing the matter of The House of Many Colors, they went on to discuss the matter of the house of "unsquare" shape and, finally, they debated the matter of the garden of many colors.

Proper procedure was followed. Nobody raised his voice above the customary and civilized level of seriousness. Nobody interrupted the speaker with any remarks and nobody made any humorous impromptu comments. Nobody differed from the previous speaker, but only added comments to support the argument. Most importantly, nobody asked any questions.

Nobody, except, of course, he with the dreaded name, The Owner of the House of Many Colors. He broke many rules in that very important meeting. He spoke with passion, which obviously caused him to raise his voice to levels way above the accepted norms.

Many of the people at the meeting felt a strange tingling surge of emotion as he spoke, but they were very disciplined in fighting such emotional temptation. The speaker made some very humorous comments which very nearly had many of the listeners burst out laughing, but once again sanity and sensibility prevailed, and they resisted the silly temptation.

He also had a line of thought which was quite different from all previous speakers and for the people in the meeting that was hard to swallow. Some of them felt almost angry, but since it was not customary for them to show anger or engage in passionate thought-provoking debate, The Owner of the House of Many Colors, in effect, had the last say in the debate.

He ended his speech with what was the worst of any rule breaking at such a meeting; he asked some very profound questions. Questioning anything, especially the status quo, was strictly forbidden at these meetings.

There was an uneasiness of coughing and raising of eyebrows, but since these people never interrupted a speaker, he was able to ask all the questions he had that day.

It was a historic day. Although the councilors were

not aware of the importance of that day, it was the first day that anybody ever asked any questions in the council meeting of The Town called Potential.

The ancient books of wisdom record these questions in great detail, and up to this day they are regarded as The Great Questions in the Battle against Conformity. On that day, in that council meeting in The Town called Potential, these simple but profound questions were asked:

The Great Questions in the Battle against Conformity

1. Why is the rainbow of hope not gray?
2. Why is an innocent child intrigued and not horrified by colors?
3. Why do the waves of the great oceans not fall on the beach in identical cubes of water?
4. Why, with each unique sunrise and sunset, does the sun not conform even to its own beauty of yesterday?
5. Why is the flame red, and why are the ashes gray?
6. In the eye of the lover, why is the beloved more beautiful than all others?
7. If the home of your soul is unique – your hands, your eyes, your smile – is he who asks you to conform not an enemy of your very soul ?

When he had finished these questions, he sat down. He gazed at his peers. His expression was one of strength but not bitterness; victory but not pride; pity but not weakness; anger but not lovelessness. He almost seemed to not only be gazing at them, but through them. He seemed to be seeing something they were unable to see. He seemed to be full of joy and full of sadness at the same time.

The councilors were very uncomfortable. They could think of only one thing to do, and that was to stick to the agenda. They did, however, allow a slight deviation from normal procedure when the time came to vote for or against the motion. None of the councilors had the desire to vote with the normal *aye* or *nay*. In the presence of The Owner of the House of Many Colors, they preferred a secret ballot. Somehow they felt convicted.

Still, when the motion was read out loud – a motion that it should be deemed illegal to build "unsquare" houses, to paint houses any color that is not the standard gray and, finally, to have any gardens other than the accepted fruit and vegetable gardens – a feeling of safety, security and stability (very important words in The Town called Potential) came over the councilors.

All of them felt much better once the votes had been counted and not one vote was against the proposed law. They knew then that The Owner of the House of Many

Colors could definitely not be right. Their vote was one of unity. How could all of them be wrong?

Consensus was a sure sign of wisdom. There could be no doubt that they did what was right for the town and its traditions. They felt that they were heroes of preservation (and, as you may have supposed, heroism was not a feeling that they often experienced). There were serious nods of approval. The day of the meeting was declared the Day of Conformity, the most important day on the calendar of The Town called Potential.

In the confidentiality of private conversations, (for no one wanted to be seen in public with The Owner of the House of Many Colors after the historic council meeting) all of the members of the council confessed to agreeing in principle with The Owner of the House of Many Colors.

They felt that although painting colorful houses was maybe not such a bad thing in itself, it was still a very radical change from the way they were used to doing things. And, of course, it was only sensible to always weigh change against the more important ideas of safety, security and stability.

In that light, they explained, they could not vote for these new ideas at that specific time, but they went to great lengths, in very long explanatory sentences, to assure The Owner of the House of Many Colors that they respected his point of view and would give it a great deal of thought and that they would, at the right time, be right beside him in his fight for change. They also asked him, for reasons they were sure he would understand, not to mention their discussions with him to anyone.

Although he was now technically in breach of the law, The Owner of the House of Many Colors was never arrested. The reason for this was, firstly, that the people of The Town called Potential were not prone to drastic behavior of any kind. Therefore there were no criminals in town. These people were of a more placid nature and did not feel that it was worth the effort or the risk to break any laws.

Secondly, in the unlikely event of anyone breaking the law, there were no police officers to arrest such an offender since policing would be deemed a dangerous profession and therefore not in line with their high regard for safety, security and stability.

So, in this first ever incident of anybody breaking any law, they decided to punish this family by avoiding contact with them as far as possible. In this way, nobody's safety would be put at risk.

Naturally, fewer and fewer people ever talked to The Owner of the House of Many Colors and his family. Not only was The Owner of the House of Many Colors now called The Strange One, but his whole family was referred to as The Strange Ones.

Still, every year on their annual house-painting day, there was a strange feeling of emptiness as they watched The Strange Ones repainting their house in the most beautiful colors. There was a feeling of longing for something different, something new, as they heard the laughter coming from the colorful house.

It was indeed a difficult day, especially as they tried to explain to their children why gray was the best color for painting a house.

... there is something right outside time and place ... Beauty is the call of the spirit in that something to the spirit in us.
C. S. Lewis

Chapter 2

Of Knowledge
and Auctions

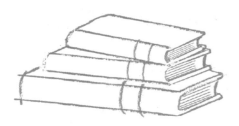

The cloke that I left at Troas with Carpus, when thou comest, bring with thee, and the books, but especially the parchments.

2 Timothy 4:13

H E WAS A great man and a man of great knowledge. He was a student of one of the most respected teachers of his time and his knowledge and wisdom far exceeded that of his peers.

He was just beginning with what was surely to be a promising career as a leader and teacher in Israel. And then he met Someone who set him on a search for true knowledge for the rest of his life.

The apostle Paul said that this Someone had hidden in Himself all the treasures of knowledge. Knowledge of creation, in fact, He was the Creator. Knowledge of life, He was the source of life. Knowledge of beauty. Of love. Of pain. Tears. Joy. And death. In Him was knowledge without limit. Knowledge beyond knowledge.

Where mere knowing stops and is engulfed by the object known, that is where Paul came to the end of all he had ever known and the beginning of what he had never known.

The taste of the depth and beauty of this knowledge made Paul a slave and a seeker for the rest of his days.

Even when he was an old man, wearied and frail from much suffering, he was still searching, wanting to know more.

Jailed and burdened, in need of the basic necessities of life, he wrote to his young friend Timothy and asked only for his cloak and his books. His search never ended.

And indeed, the only search worthwhile, is the kind that never ends.

> O world invisible, we view thee,
> O world intangible, we touch thee,
> O world unknowable, we know thee,
> Inapprehensible, we clutch thee!
> *Francis Thomson*

Our hero was such a man. He knew that life affords us opportunities to gain understanding. He understood true knowledge and wisdom to be like books on auction in the library of life.

These auctions are frequent occasions, but one can easily pass by them without noticing. In fact, very few people ever attend them, because few even know about them. If you don't visit the library, you won't know about the auction.

Of course a library is not necessarily a building where books are being stored. We are referring here to the library of life; that great storeroom of wisdom which can be found daily if our eyes are open to see it and our hearts are willing to search for it.

This library of life can teach us wisdom as we make it our aim to learn from every situation, from every person and from all creation and ultimately from Him in whom all knowledge resides. Those who are truly searching will come to the source of knowledge.

[May you come] unto all riches of the full assurance of understanding, to the acknowledgement of the mystery of God, and of the Father, and of Christ; in whom are hid all the treasures of wisdom and knowledge.

COLOSSIANS 2:2-3

You will find our hero and his family to be amongst those who are humble enough to be permitted to make use of the library exclusively for those who never want to stop learning.

There are rules for bidding at the auctions of the library of life. We have to ask ourselves if we would be willing, as were our hero and his family, to obey these ancient rules for bidding at these auctions:

Three Rules for Bidding
at Library Auctions

1. Your own insight must never be your main source of wisdom.
   The fool's own knowledge is his master, and he the slave of his ignorance.

2. **Wisdom is to be valued above riches.**

   What gold is there that can pay for wisdom? None.
   What gold is there that wisdom cannot buy? None.

3. **Be careful about what you regard as wisdom.**

   After he had learned that his lunch was poisoned, the fool
   rejoiced that it was at least tasty and presently had another
   serving. He died with a full stomach.

As we witness the desire for true knowledge in the heart of the hero of our story, we are reminded of the words of another wise man who ages ago pointed us in the direction of this life-long search:

> *The heart of him that hath understanding seeketh know-*
> *ledge ... Wise men lay up knowledge ... When wisdom*
> *entereth into thine heart, and knowledge is pleasant unto*
> *thy soul; discretion shall preserve thee, understanding shall*
> *keep thee ... Through wisdom is an house builded; and by*
> *understanding it is established: And by knowledge shall*
> *the chambers be filled with all precious and pleasant riches.*
> *A wise man is strong; yea, a man of knowledge increaseth*
> *strength.*
>
> PROVERBS 15:14; 10:14; 2:10-11; 24:3-5

the unwanted library

ITT WAS TRULY a grand old building – definitely much older than the rest of the buildings in town. This was evident from the fact that it had the most beautiful gables and elaborate artwork of ancient sculptors on the walls, staircases of the finest wood and copper, and chandeliers of gold and crystal hanging from the roof. And of course its design was much more intricate than that of the countless square-shaped buildings in The Town called Potential.

One could sense that it was a building of stature and

that many great people had gathered in it for great discussions, concerts and art exhibitions.

Even the smell was that wonderful smell of old buildings with old books full of old, beautiful and mysterious stories, lessons and histories. Just entering the grand old library made one feel strangely wise and aware of the feeling that if one could remain for long enough, one would discover secrets so deep and so important.

It almost seemed as if these secrets could help to solve all mysteries and enchant the hearts of all people who long for deep and beautiful things. It was truly very sad that the beautiful old building was covered with thick layers of dull, gray paint …

Very few people visited the library. The people of The Town called Potential were of the opinion (and when they were of an opinion it was nearly impossible to make them listen to any other opinion) that reading too many books would just tempt them to change their opinion, and in their opinion that was a very risky thing to do.

New ideas meant that they would have to attempt new things, maybe even dangerous things or things that they had no knowledge of. That might make them feel uninformed, and feeling uninformed was such an uncomfortable feeling. They were of the opinion that new ideas, but also very old ideas, were quite discomforting.

Ancient knowledge had so much mystery about it – it

spoke of such deep things as death and bravery and far-away places, the ends of the earth and the beginnings of the heavens. Why, these things could cause one to want to travel!

Maybe one would even try to understand the beginnings of all things, and everybody knew that that was impossible, and of course attempting the impossible was a very ambitious and foolish thing to do. As a rule they avoided ambitious and foolish ventures.

So it came about that the only knowledge that they deemed to be wholesome and safe was the knowledge that they already had.

Nothing about their own knowledge was too new or too old, nothing too mysterious or too challenging. Their own knowledge, nothing more and nothing less, could be of greater help to them to keep things exactly as they were.

Nothing from the ancient past could threaten them, neither could anything from the future scare them. And that was just the way they wanted things to be: safe, secure and stable.

The Owner of the House of Many Colors and his family were the only people who ever visited the ancient library. Somehow it just worked that way with them; the more they longed for beautiful things, the more they wanted to spend time trying to understand ancient truths. Wonder and searching, beauty and wisdom, seemed to them to go hand in hand. Both the experience of beholding beauty and discovering truth left them with a stab of joy in their hearts. But, inevitably, too soon the wound of joy would heal and they would again go into that blissful battle in search of beauty and truth.

Some other things also walked hand in hand for The Owner of the House of Many Colors and his family who ever so keenly followed the example of their hero of a father and husband.

People could not understand them. Quite frankly, they thought The Strange Ones, living in their strange house, to be quite disconnected from reality. The reason was that the family, so enchanted by their search for beauty and knowledge, seemed to be unable to decide in which century they wanted to live.

Sometimes they seemed to be talking as if all that really mattered were those things of which they had read in the ancient books of wisdom: ancient laws, ancient stories and ancient mysteries – even ancient music, works of art and ancient plays.

They would speak in riddles about how no people could live if they were not connected to time gone by. About how the past had to be the foundation for the future of those who wished to truly live life.

And then on other days The Strange Ones would

speak as if nothing mattered in all the world except "this day"; the beauty of this day, the joy and opportunities, the people and challenges of this day.

Once again they would speak in riddles of how the past can have no hold on those who live fully for today. They would assure their confused listeners that fears of tomorrow are conquered and the chains of yesterday broken by the passionate embrace of today.

And then again came those days that they acted and talked as if nothing but the future mattered. Their riddle-filled eulogies of the joy of living for tomorrow explained how, with the unstoppable power of destiny and hope, tomorrow would lure anyone who believed in it.

They exclaimed how no mountains of today could be high enough to keep the pilgrims en route to tomorrow captive in the status quo of today's comforts or pains.

Indeed, according to the people of The Town called Potential, The Strange Ones were to be pitied. Their minds had surely been confused by the ancient ideas of primitive authors and by their infatuation with new ideas.

Surely, their being so different was a sign that they were on a wrong and dangerous road. Their preposterous ideas were shared by no one in the community. How could any one risk going against the majority?

With time, the ancient library became more and more

a serious point of discussion during the meetings of the town council. They felt that the library belonged to the people and should therefore reflect the culture. All the other buildings, except The House of Many Colors, were square and gray. The library was just too much of a grand old building. There were too many gables on the exterior and too many elaborate works of art and chandeliers of gold and crystal in the interior.

The time had come for the library to be stripped of all these things that made it so different.

The town council also felt that the library could be put to better use than storing ancient books of wisdom. They decided to get rid of all the books which, according to them, were useless anyway. They reasoned that since nobody, except The Owner of the House of Many Colors and his family ever read these books, they could not contain any wisdom that could be of any use to them.

They also wanted to protect their children from the influence of the books which obviously had a very strange effect on the only family who ever read them.

It was officially decided that all the books in the library should be auctioned so that the library could be put to better use, after its official renovation to new appropriate sameness.

It was a strange auction indeed. The people were addressed and asked what anybody would be willing to pay for the ancient books of wisdom.

The Owner of the House of Many Colors answered that he would be willing to give his house and all his possessions. Then there was a stunned silence and the people whispered to one another their amazement that anyone would be willing to pay anything for the useless old books. One could see their genuine pity for The poor Owner of The House of Many Colors.

Then there was silence and not a single bid followed that of The Owner of the House of Many Colors.

The auctioneer had a word with the town councilors who refused the bid of The Owner of the House of Many Colors. They had even less use for an "unsquare", multi-colored, flower-gardened house than for the ancient books of wisdom.

They decided that since there was no other bid, and since The Owner of the House of Many Colors had already offered all that he possessed, the books would not be for sale any longer. Instead, the library would be left open for the day and anybody who wished to do so could take the books.

They did, however, warn the people that it would be illegal, after the next official meeting of the town council, to own any of the ancient books of wisdom. This, they said, should not be seen as a restrictive law, but a protective one and after this explanation there were serious nods of approval throughout the room.

Of course, the problem of getting rid of the books could easily have been solved, had they only decided to destroy them, but for these people that would have been quite a drastic measure.

There was also the danger that there could be a curse on anyone destroying these ancient books and although they did not really believe in ancient and outdated theories about curses, it was not worth the risk.

All the people went home, thankful that they had a council with such wisdom – all the people except The Owner of the House of Many Colors and his family. They worked all day to take every single book from the library to their house. At the end of the day the whole house was filled with books and the The Strange Ones immediately drew up plans to extend the house.

For the next few months they were happy to break the law again and build a room bigger than the rest of the house in which to put the ancient books of wisdom. They were now the legal owners of the books which had been declared illegal to own.

Their multicolored, "unsquare" house became even more "unsquare" and they created artful blends and combinations of colors to their hearts' delight for their grand library. The citizens of the gray section were deeply offended, but the children at play were secretly building magnificent, colorful mansions and imagined that they were reading ancient books full of bravery and wisdom in their "un-gray" world of dreams and wonder.

And oh, the magic of going to sleep at night knowing that one day their world might be less gray, less square and, yes, maybe even exciting, if not dangerous.

All the while, their parents were lying awake at night wondering how to guide their children on the tried and trusted ways of safety, security and stability ...

The town council frowned upon yet another sign of disrespect for the law from The Owner of the House of Many Colors and his family. These breakers of the law were therefore ignored all the more by the people of The Town called Potential.

However, the members of the council were relieved that it was The Strange Ones, and nobody else in town who took the books, since this family had already been indoctrinated beyond any rehabilitation.

They now also had the empty library at their disposal. It was nearly time for the annual house painting day and they wanted to stock up some gray paint. They felt that since the ancient building was a library, there should at least be some useful modern books in the library.

For this reason they commissioned all the wisest people in town to write a book about the proper methods for painting one's house with the standard gray paint. The official opening of the newly-stocked library was a grand occasion with, once again, serious nods of approval.

The man of the present acts prudently from the
example of the past, so as not to imperil the future.
Titian

Chapter 3

Of Beginnings, Consequences and Endings

For they are a nation void of counsel, neither is there any understanding in them. O that they were wise, that they understood this, that they would consider their latter end!

Deuteronomy 32:28-29

NE WONDERS HOW they could do it. They had seen some of the most spectacular, supernatural actions of God. They had experienced His miraculous hand leading them out of slavery in Egypt. How could they ever forget the dry ground in the middle of great waters, God's appearance on the mountain, His voice from the thunder and the manna in the desert?

They had seen His fury in the death of the rebels amongst them. And yet, so soon after witnessing the mighty hand of God, they turned to idol worship. How was that possible?

It happened as it does with all wrong paths that we take. Small compromises. Turning only slightly from the way. The poison of darkness is a slow poison. Getting lost one step at a time.

> Indeed the safest road to Hell is the gradual one –
> the gentle slope, soft underfoot, without sudden
> turnings, without milestones, without signposts ...
> *C. S. Lewis*

As we again join the people from the ancient town in our story we will be wise not to think of them as unusually daft or unwise. In their doings we might recognize our own mistakes.

Is it not so that in all our tragic endeavors we enjoy

the pleasures of beginnings, not remembering that all seeds grow to be trees and will bear fruit? In the secret of dark shadows we forget that the sun will rise again and its light has no respect for secrets. We forget that both the darkness of night and the light of day come to us almost unnoticed.

When we turn slightly from the way, we are in very dangerous territory. Being still close to the way, we do not realize that we are in danger.

Our hero, however, was aware of the danger of deception – the danger of thinking one is safe, not realizing one's life is in jeopardy. He understood that the wrong way is mostly more attractive than the way of truth.

Often the way to death is vibrant with things seeming like life itself, yet having within them the poison of death.

There is a way which seemeth right unto a man, but the end thereof are the ways of death.

PROVERBS 14:12

Our story is concerned with the danger of entertaining small dragons. We are reminded of ancient wisdom warning us about the dragon of all dragons, the serpent of evil. His ways are not only of such cunning that we do not notice his evil, but even more twisted is his deception, making us mistake evil for good.

Warnings come to us about this, the deepest of all deception, mistaking evil for good. Note in our story how the warnings of wisdom were discarded as foolishness and be reminded of wise words of warning concerning the age-old deception:

> *Satan himself is transformed into an angel of light. Therefore it is no great thing if his ministers also be transformed as the ministers of righteousness; whose end shall be according to their works.*
>
> 2 CORINTHIANS 11:14-15

We will be wise to pause and think about cute little dragons and answer some questions. We have already learned that the artists of life are they who are brave enough to ask questions when the majority is silent. We have learned that wisdom is available to those who seek it. We now have to learn that it is necessary also to answer the questions that we so easily shy away from. Many of these questions are questions concerning our own secret little dragons.

Our story might prompt us to listen carefully and hear the strange nagging questions of the heart about secrets and compromises:

Three Questions about Little Dragons

1. **What will this pet be when it has grown up?**

   Many are the joys that grow up to be miseries.
   Blessed is he who has learned that some dragons appear to be darlings and some darlings appear to be dragons. More blessed still, when he has learned to know one from the other.

2. **Who will kill your dragons if you don't?**

   If a man is not brave enough to kill a mosquito today, what will make him brave enough to kill a lion tomorrow?

3. **What dragons keep returning to your life?**

   Oh, wretched cage of secrets, how foolish was I to think that the key of time would not unlock thee!

knowing darlings
from dragons

DURING A PARTICULARLY long, dark and cold winter, the almost wonderful, vaguely beautiful, very nearly ingenious and definitely very precious people of The Town called Potential were in very great danger of being forever annihilated.

The danger came from the mountain overlooking the town. This great mountain was called Mount Possibility, but some of the very ancient books referred to it as Mount Royal, and to its highest peak as The Peak of Great Challenge. The name Mount Royal was a mystery to the people, because they had no king. They could also not remember a time when there had ever been one and were quite certain that none of them were of royal descent.

They felt that the name Mount Impossibility would have been much more appropriate than the name Mount Possibility, since it was impossible to climb to the highest peak, or even only to the higher regions.

How they arrived at the conclusion that it was impossible, was never established. They had obviously not read it in the ancient books. They had not tried to climb the mountain and had no desire to do so.

The only opinion they could go by was that of The Owner of the House of Many Colors, and his opinion was of course tainted by the foolish and out-dated ideas in his ancient books.

It was very logical then that since The Owner of the House of Many Colors believed it was possible to conquer Mount Possibility, and since everybody knew that his thinking had gone pitifully wrong, they were quite correct in considering it impossible to climb the mountain.

What concerns us now is not the opinions about the names of the mountain or who thought that they could climb it or not. We are more interested in certain inhabitants of the high and mysterious Mount Possibility. One creature dwelling there was thought to be the fiercest of all the dragons of ancient times; Dragon Mediocrity ...

At first, the people of The Town called Potential were not at all afraid of this dragon. In fact, there was a time that it was living among them and everybody was treating it as a pet.

It mysteriously arrived in town one day. It even had a beautiful chain around its neck and on the chain a tag with its name written on it in their ancient language. The name, Mediocrity, could have two different meanings in this ancient tongue.

One meaning would be: "that which speaks of the balance between eagerness and wisdom, an attitude that can save one from many tears and dangers – one of the valuable treasures of the soul."

The other meaning was more sinister: "that which speaks of a lack of will-power, decisiveness and courage – an attitude that can be the cause of many tears and much regret, preventing one from reaching one's true potential – one of the dangerous beasts that threaten the soul."

The Owner of the House of Many Colors warned the people of The Town called Potential that in the history recorded in the ancient books of wisdom there had never been any dragons, good or bad, that were *not* dangerous. It was clear that Mediocrity in this case could have no meaning other than the second, more sinister meaning.

Of course, this was yet again enough proof to the people that the dragon could definitely *not* be dangerous. It was becoming so easy to establish what was true or not; they simply had to hear what The Owner of the House of Many Colors was thinking and then disagree with it.

In a sense, the town council was beginning to rely very much on his opinions. They were even talking of how ingenious it was of them to allow him to take the ancient books home.

So it came about that these people, in their almost kind and very nearly loving way, started feeding and taking care of the baby Dragon Mediocrity. (Even dragons, in fact, especially dragons, are at first very cute babies, before they become what they really are.) They treated the dragon as if it were indeed, as they were convinced its name indicated, a valuable treasure.

At that time, Mediocrity, the playful little dragon, loved all the attention. People noticed that he smiled whenever his name was affectionately called out. This was very strange; even these people knew that it was unheard of for dragons to smile. The Owner of the House of Many Colors reminded them of an ancient proverb which sent shivers down their spines (although nobody would admit it):

Beware the wink of evil eyes
They promise life, deliver lies
Beware the smile of evil breath
Its teeth are white as bones of death

Even for a growing baby dragon it had a very healthy appetite. Everybody thought that the little dragon with the healthy appetite and playful nature was very cute; everybody except The Owner of the House of Many Colors. He was accused of not being an animal lover, but of course this was not true. He had always been known to be very fond of animals.

He was also accused of being a pessimist who saw evil and danger in everything, but we all know by now that there was not a greater optimist in town than The Owner of the House of Many Colors.

He had a good reason to be very sceptical about the dragon. In all the ancient stories about dragons he had never read of any dragon, good or evil, big or small, who did not instil fear in those who first met it. Respect, caution, and terror were feelings one felt in the presence of dragons.

Ancient wisdom even taught that good dragons were to be feared more than bad ones, because for friend or foe there was no escape from their pursuit. Why then, if all dragons were very dangerous, did Mediocrity try so hard to be a playful and harmless little pet?

Although he sent out numerous letters of warning to every address in town, nobody believed what he had to say. His warnings about the danger of entertaining cute little dragons were regarded as the fanatic preaching of a man befuddled by mysterious ancient books.

There was a growing pity for him and whenever he or his family was mentioned in any discussion, people would just shake their heads in sympathy for a man who had so lost track of modern times.

Mediocrity, the cute little dragon, soon became such a popular animal in The Town called Potential, that they made a statue in honor of him and placed this statue in front of their gray library. It was to remind them that they were modern people, liberated from the dangerous teachings of ancient wisdom, keeping in high regard only those ancient customs that ensured their safety, security and stability. Inscribed above the door behind the statue were the words: *In Honor of Mediocrity*.

Needless to say, the smile of the friendly dragon was more prominent than ever. Many had forgotten, but some remembered the ancient proverb about an evil smile and desperately hoped that it was really just ancient nonsense.

But, somehow, for the people of The Town called Potential, the words "ancient nonsense" were beginning to sound less appropriate than the words "ancient wisdom".

As time went by, Mediocrity grew a little bigger, but was still rather cute. Mysterious things started happening. One by one, the children began disappearing from the playground on the outskirts of The Town called Potential.

At first, nobody would believe The Owner of the House of Many Colors when he said that Mediocrity was responsible for it. However, some of the children reported that the cute little dragon had been hurting them and so another meeting was called in the town hall.

The Owner of the House of Many Colors proposed a very drastic measure. He had no doubt that, in accordance with ancient wisdom, the dragon should be killed. Of course, this was a measure far too drastic for the people of The Town called Potential.

However, they decided, just for the sake of safety, security and stability, to ban Mediocrity from town. Even this was the most drastic decision the town council had ever taken. Killing Mediocrity was definitely out of the question, since their honor as men of justice was at stake. And even if they did think that the dragon should be killed, the task of killing it was too dangerous for them to risk their citizens' safety.

Besides, there was no clear evidence that Mediocrity was responsible for the disappearance of the children, and they felt that banning him was already very harsh. In the light of the importance of safety, security and stability, they felt justified to take such drastic and unheard-of measures.

In the opinion of the town council, the safest and most reasonable thing to do, was to take Mediocrity to the middle regions of the mountain. (Of course, it would have been safer to take Mediocrity high up into the mountain, but the people of The Town called Potential were very afraid of high places. They felt very unsafe, insecure and unstable in such places. And anyway, was it not impossible to climb up to the higher regions of the mountain?)

Since he was still a young dragon, he would not be able to find his way down the mountain back to town, and once he got used to living in the mountain, they reasoned, he would not want to return.

The Owner of the House of Many Colors warned them that dragons always returned to those who fed them when they were young. He read to them an ancient verse from *The Song of the Forsaken Dragon* and tried to convince them that all of the ancient wisdom about dragons warned that the most dangerous of the evil dragons were those who had been befriended.

There was no way to get away from them, other than by death; either that of the dragon or that of those who had befriended it. He repeated the ancient verse in every corner of the town.

Oh hand that fed me, feed me still
Or hunger, yet, shall make me kill
Oh heart that loved me, love me more
Or shun me and I'll break thy door

He pleaded with them to slay the dragon, but to no avail. He assured them that if they all stood together with one purpose and one heart, they could slay the dragon.

The thought of fighting (even with a friendly young dragon like Mediocrity) did not appeal to them at all. Ancient poetry was ignored yet again.

They were quite nervous to break the news of the banning to Mediocrity. They explained to him how enjoyable it would be for him to live in the mountain. To their great relief, their fears that he would protest did not come true. Smilingly, and with great understanding, he assured them that he had sympathy for their concerns about his clumsiness when playing with the children. He explained that it had anyway never been his intention to stay in town for very long. Why, dragons and humans should not live together, should they? (One would almost think that the dragon was very eager to go and live in the mountain, that he would not mind living in dark, secret places from where he would plan and execute his evil deeds, in fact, that is exactly what The Owner of the House of Many Colors had predicted.)

So it came about that Dragon Mediocrity lived on Mount Royal, called Mount Possibility, somewhere in the middle region, and some distance below The Peak of Great Challenge.

During a particularly long, dark and cold winter, the almost wonderful, vaguely beautiful, very nearly ingenious and definitely (although not really aware of it) very precious people of The Town called Potential were in very great danger of being forever annihilated. Mediocrity had by then already grown to be very huge and was one of the fiercest of all the dragons.

As Mediocrity grew larger and larger he began destroying the middle region of the mountain in search of food. This had serious consequences for The Town called Potential. Mediocrity would so ruin the forest, that trees and rocks started preventing the water from flowing down to the town. Slowly but surely their crisis became more severe. The dam near the town was nearing a dreadfully empty state.

The poor town people had no idea what to do. All they could hope for was a miracle, but these people were not really of the miracle-believing kind. Miracles, if they existed at all, were very unusual, and believing in them would certainly require unusual courage and faith in things unknown. They strongly believed that things unknown had better remain unknown.

Even in the midst of very trying circumstances, and especially in the midst of trying circumstances, they felt that it would be safest to hold on to those things they were certain of. And one thing was definitely certain: they had never ventured into any of the dangerous regions of the mountain and were not about to do so now.

One would think that by now they would have believed in what The Owner of the House of Many Colors had to say, but, strangely, they acted as if it was his fault that they had almost no water. (If it hadn't been that these people were known as humble and peace-loving people, one would almost have suspected that they were rather stubborn, self-righteous and proud.)

They refused to admit that it was Mediocrity who caused all the damage to the mountain. Some even suggested that The Strange Ones could be responsible. Was it not they who were so obsessed with building things?

Where did they get all their material from? Surely it was they who had caused the damage, in search of rocks and timber to build with.

Speculation was rife but how would they know the facts if they could not spend time on the mountain to investigate? Obviously, that was out of the question. How they wished for a solution and how they hoped that the dam would somehow not become completely empty. And all the while the agony brought about a suspicion that they were far from being safe, secure or stable.

The most agonizing experience of all was that sometimes at night there would be a fierce dragon in town. Nobody knew what it looked like, since all of them were hiding in their gray, square houses. (And still they refused to admit that it could be dear old Mediocrity.)

Fortunately, they had not built these houses themselves, because the people of The Town called Potential were not known to be very hard workers. Their houses were centuries old and had been built with huge solid rocks and had heavy copper doors. No one could enter when these doors were locked, not even the fiercest of dragons, good or bad.

Even so, every now and then, someone would be caught outside on such a night, never to be seen alive again. It was terrible to hear the monstrous roars and the last pleas for mercy. Then the ugly sounds of crushing bones and appalling swallows would be followed by a deadly silence after the monster had disappeared into the black of night.

The devil hath power to assume a pleasing shape.
William Shakespeare

Chapter 4

Of Storms, Voices and Purposes

O afflicted city, lashed by storms and not comforted, I will build you with stones of turquoise, your foundations with sapphires.

ISAIAH 54:11 (NIV)

SIMPLE ANSWERS HAVE always been offered for the tough questions of life. Easy solutions; if only they could solve problems, but they do not. The sages peddling these black-and-white formulas can certainly make us feel good as long as things are going well. As soon as problems land on our doorstep, these simple philosophies give us high hopes, but only until we hit the dead-end street of reality.

Israel had many such soothsayers. When the people of God had departed from Him, there were still those who prophesied prosperity. There was a shallow and superficial spirituality, mixed with idolatry and exploitation. Yet, the blessings of God were the theme of every sermon.

When the true prophets warned that God was threatening with storms of purging, they were ridiculed and persecuted. Their message did not fit the theme of the day: "Good God – good times, hallelujah for the easy life!"

Isaiah's hard and unpopular message was in the end the one that stood the test of time. And, ironically, after the storms he had predicted had indeed come, he was the one to predict God's blessing. The promise was that the God who sent the storm was the God who would bring restoration and riches beyond measure.

Life, the kind of life that God gives, is like that: destiny never precedes purging. Those who would reach the destiny purposed for them, would first have to go through fire.

O bless our God, ye people ... For Thou, O God, hast proved us: Thou hast tried us, as silver is tried ... We went through fire and through water: but Thou broughtest us out into a wealthy place.

PSALM 66:8, 10, 12

We would be wise to follow the example of our hero and notice how he was able not only to endure the storm, but to hear the voice beyond the noise of troubling winds. This voice cannot be heard by those who want only ease and comfort; it is a voice for those who are willing to pay the price to reach the high places of destiny.

Indeed, there is more to a storm than hardship; every storm has a voice, a calling. Simple theology says of that voice that it is evil. It has an idea that God's blessings exclude hardship; that hardship comes only from the dark side.

This idea makes for a predictable, comfortable God. But the God of the Bible loves too much to not be dangerous. *If your God is safe, before whom will you tremble?* God is God of both storm and calm. And even when the Evil One does send a storm, (for there are such storms) the God we are talking about has enough authority, power and wisdom to use the most evil of storms to serve His purposes.

And so, we have to learn to find the purpose in storms, even if the purpose is only to learn that we are unable to understand all things. Yes, to accept the reality that there are mysteries beyond our comprehension is one of the great purposes that storms can achieve in our minds, minds that are so addicted to answers.

The ignorant will tell you that it is an easy task to understand storms, and of course step one in their scheme would be not to allow for God's initiative and purpose. To believe them will bring you much disappointment.

To be one of those who allow the storms of life to take them to higher places will make of you a finder of purpose, and much is required of such a person.

Five Things Required of a Finder of Purpose:

1. A finder of purpose must allow storms to do their work.
   It is not for the nature of the storm, but for the nature of a man, to determine whether he will experience destruction or receive instruction. This, indeed, is effected by the choice of a man, but choose as he may, the storm will come.

2. A finder of purpose must very rarely return to the safety of the status quo.

Lady Status Quo's lover will never be disappointed, never be betrayed … never be excited and, alas, never be alive.

3. A finder of purpose must run his race, not against those in front of him, nor against those next to him, or behind him. His race is against himself.
    Why are you not searching for the treasure, my son?
    I have no map, my father.
    You need only a mirror.

4. A finder of purpose should see with the eyes of tomorrow.
    Many are they who open their eyes in order to see what is in front of them, few are they who close their eyes in order to see beyond.

5. A finder of purpose must so act in the storm that the calm will benefit him.
    If you cannot live like a king in the ghettos, then, even in a palace you will live like a beggar.

Blessed is the man who perseveres under trial, because when he has stood the test, he will receive the crown of life that God has promised to those who love him.

JAMES 1:12 (NIV)

strange winds
and secret palaces

TO OVERCOME GREAT fear is very difficult, but thirst goes a long way in helping with this problem. Although the people of The Town called Potential were tormented day and night by the very thought of how many of their children, friends and family had disappeared and also by the nightly visitations of the cruel monster, they still needed water to drink, if they wanted to stay alive at all.

As they were watching the dam become only a muddy hole in the ground, they realized that their troubles were mounting and that they would soon have to make decisions they had wished they would never have to make.

And so, driven by thirst, the people of The Town called Potential were forced to go to places they had never been to before. To them the middle regions of Mount Possibility were high ground that they had no desire to frequent. None of them had ever been there, and there were now so many rumors of dangerous dragons in the mountain that the drying up of the dam could not have come at a more inopportune time. By now there were even those who suggested that Mediocrity may not have been such a friendly dragon after all.

Even so, regardless of what one thought of Mediocrity, safety, security, stability, or for that matter, miracles, ancient books of wisdom, libraries, or colorful houses; the time had come to take a risk or die.

The members of the town council felt that they had a responsibility to make sure that the women and children in town were safe. They assured everyone that they would not even think of shifting such a dangerous responsibility onto anyone else. They knew that they had a duty and wanted everyone to know that they could rely on them as leaders to do that duty no matter what it would take.

It was obvious to these members of the council that they would, in the light of their dangerous duty to protect the women and children, not be able to assist in any water-fetching duties.

In a courageous and unselfish gesture, the other men from The Town called Potential thanked the council members for their deep sense of duty, but assured them rather forcefully that it was too high a risk for the town to lose their council in case of an attack on the town while the other men were on their water-fetching duties.

The council protested, but somehow it became clear to them that it might just become more dangerous for them to attempt to stay in town than to venture on to the mountain.

The non-council members shook their heads in deep disappointment with The Owner of the House of Many Colors when he volunteered to go with the council into the mountain. How could he leave the town at such a dangerous time? They protested, but in such a way as to not really dissuade him. They were quite willing to protect the women and children all by themselves, but found it scandalous that anyone could abandon duty and be so afraid of danger.

The council members, on the other hand, were obviously relieved. Somehow they suspected, although they would never admit it, that this was a time when knowledge of ancient things would be helpful.

And so came the departure to territories unknown. It

was a beautiful morning, but with thirst driving them and with fear of dangerous monsters that could attack them at any moment, no-one cared particularly much about the beauty of the morning.

The council members were quick to point out to The Owner of the House of Many Colors that the unavoidable attack was sure to come from the back, but that they were willing to take the dangerous rearguard. The Owner of the House of Many Colors thanked them for their bravery, but even being praised for bravery made them feel deeply ashamed. It was not long into their journey when they found the blockage in the stream going to the dam. They thought that they might die of thirst, when in fact their solution was quite within reach.

They had just quenched their thirst and cleared the blockage when a strange wind started blowing.

All around them it grew mysteriously dark. Suddenly they had no idea which was the direction back home. The ominous wind was blowing stronger and stronger. As if forced by the power of the wind, they went higher and higher into the mountain until they were in places filled with mist and ancient trees.

All the men were only aware of monsters and a howling gale, but The Owner of the House of Many Colors was aware of something extraordinary. From somewhere came a voice that was not the voice of a man. He heard the wind blowing, but from within the blowing sound came a voice, the breathing voice of the wind. He heard something that reminded him of a poem in one of the ancient books of wisdom. The wind repeated over and over:

in the wind there is a voice
wherein kings and queens rejoice
follow me
oh follow me
come to find
your destiny
what you do when windstorms rage
makes you royalty or slave

When the storm was at its fiercest the men had no idea what to do or where to go to, only The Owner of the House of Many Colors seemed to have no doubt at all. All the others just followed him higher up Mount Royal to places they had never in their wildest dreams imagined they would go – not that they ever really had any dreams of this kind. Higher and higher they went, until the wind suddenly calmed down to only a gentle breeze.

The silence after the mysterious storm was almost tangible; the kind of silence that makes one afraid to breathe.

This deep kind of silence brings one to a place of hearing only the most important voices in the universe – voices of darkness and voices of light. These men were now entering this ominous silence. Each one of them could feel and hear his heart beating. They completely stopped thinking about evil dragons, but not about danger. In fact, all of them, including The Owner of the House of Many Colors, were more afraid than they had ever been, but it was a fear of a different kind.

Most of us normally avoid silence because deep within us we know that there we meet with old things. Eternal things.

The Owner of the House of Many Colors knew that this was the silence that was mentioned in so many of the ancient books of wisdom. This was the dreaded Silence of Meaning of which it was said that it would fall on every heart, and only the wise would not be harmed by it.

In this, the Silence of Meaning, all men were to come to the crossroads leading to life or death.

It was written that all men would fear this silence, but some would grow to both fear and love it and others to fear and loathe it. In the love of the Silence of Meaning were the beginnings of the roads to life and in the loathing of the Silence, the roads to death.

Everything looked so ancient. It seemed to the men,

huddled together as if surrounded by an unseen enemy, that the silence was getting louder by the minute.

When the mist had cleared, they found themselves in what long before then must have been a magnificent garden. As far as the eye could see, there were statues and porches and rows and rows of majestic trees and big lawns and fountains and fish-ponds. In the distance they thought they could see what looked like a palace.

There was no gale anymore, only silence and an ancient world. The silence reminded The Owner of the House of Many Colors of times back in The Town called Potential when he had stood alone. Times when he wished that there would be voices that agreed with him, but when his expectation was met with only another kind of silence. He remembered how he had to choose in those moments of silence. He remembered the temptation to join with those who refused to make difficult choices.

And now, once again, the silence was there and also the temptation to succumb to the temptation of ease. But his was a mind that had been strengthened by smaller difficult choices. He faced the dilemma of exploring this strange and ancient place or of going back to the safety of familiar places. He knew that there was only one choice for him.

The other men were not so eager to follow The Owner

of the House of Many Colors as he headed straight for the mysterious palace. They thought that it might be more appropriate (especially in the light of their safety, security and stability) to have a meeting and discuss the best way to get back to town, to thick walls and familiar faces. How they longed for familiar things like council meetings, protocol, long discussions and the satisfaction of making important decisions that secured the status quo. The thought of a council meeting made them want to get away from the strangeness of the ancient place as soon as humanly possible. In fact, they decided to have a council meeting right there and then.

There were some senior council members in the party and one of them was duly nominated as chairman of the committee to get them down the mountain and back to their dearly beloved and familiar old town.

The appointed chairman promptly made a beautiful speech, thanking the rest of the party for their confidence in him and also thanking his wife, in her absence, for years of loyal support and faith in him. She was his inspiration. She had always been telling him that he was definitely not chairman material, but considering the abilities of the other council members, there was no reason for him to tire himself with more effort in his work.

If any one of them, being as average as they were,

could become a chairman, then so could he. She had no doubt that he would someday be a chairman, at least as competent (or incompetent) as any other chairman of the town council.

He assured them that he would do what was necessary to get them back to town without risking their safety or his own. And then there were serious nods of approval from all his devoted followers.

Not surprisingly, they got down the mountain fairly easily. Getting down from mountains seemed to be much easier for the people of The Town called Potential than getting up there.

Just after their arrival, during a special meeting of the town council, the chairman of the Down-the-Mountain Committee received a certificate for good service. His wife was really proud of him.

He refused the offer of the first ever gold watch for bravery in The Town called Potential. This was not an easy decision. Deep down, there was nothing that he desired more than to be honored in this manner; all the nods of approval, being asked what time it was during council meetings while staring at his watch just long enough to remind the other not-so-brave councilors of his greatness. The stories the children would be telling one another about his fearless expedition in the high mountain.

How he longed to be different, how he longed to be like (yes, the thought seemed outrageous) The Strange One. He almost accepted the gold watch, but the risk was just too big that some real bravery might then be expected of him during the nightly visitations of the monster.

Fortunately, there were once again serious nods of approval as he was praised for his great humility in refusing such an honor.

While the Down-the-Mountain Committee was having its meeting, The Owner of the House of Many Colors arrived at what turned out to be a palace of such magnitude that he could not think of having read about a palace of this kind in any of his ancient books. Of course there was the one great mysterious palace, but this could surely not be it ... or could it?

In a book full of ancient laws and sayings about kings and slaves called *The Book of Separation*, a palace was mentioned in a chapter with the title: *Of Choices, Attitudes and Dwelling Places*. The name of the palace was never mentioned in the book. It was written only that it was "the palace prepared for many, chosen by few." Its location was described only as "the high places." The route there was "the road through the storm, seen only by eyes that look beyond."

As The Owner of the House of Many Colors looked at the palace, something about it looked very familiar. At first he could not think what it was. And then he noticed the colors of the palace. They were the same as the colors of his house in The Town called Potential, or rather, the same as he had always intended them to be. After he had painted his house every year, he always liked it very much, but kept feeling like an artist with an unfinished painting. Here, for the first time, was the finished product.

And somehow he felt that he had painted the palace.

God passes through the thicket of the world,
and wherever his glance falls he turns all things to beauty.
John of the Cross

Chapter 5

Of Closed Doors and Dark Nights

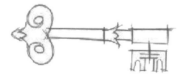

Faith which does not doubt is dead Faith.

MIGUEL DE UNAMUNO

They that sow in tears shall reap in joy. He that goeth forth and weepeth, bearing precious seed, shall doubtless come again with rejoicing, bringing his sheaves with him.

PSALM 126:5-6

HIS SUIT OF clothing was bordering on the extravagant. The size of his gold ring attested to the fact that he believed that faith and riches went hand in hand. The television host asked how this famous preacher and best-selling author handled it when those days of gloom came his way. Triumphantly he simply stated that he lived in permanent joy, for such was the command of Paul in Philippians 4:4: "Rejoice in the Lord always: and again I say, Rejoice."

As a very young believer I was amazed at that. For some time afterwards I felt that I must be very weak and sinful, and wondered when I would come to be a man of such faith that I could experience permanent joy, let alone have enough money to buy such a ring!

Let us consider for a moment Paul's instruction that followers of Christ should always rejoice. This very same apostle of faith reminds the elders of the church in Ephesus of his own life and example:

And when they were come to him, he said unto them, ye know, from the first day that I came into Asia, after what manner I have been with you at all seasons, serving the Lord with all humility of mind, and with many tears, and temptations, which befell me by the lying in wait of the Jews.

ACTS 20:18-19

It seems then that true joy, far from being a constant flow of triumphant praises and a permanent smile, may have more to do with an attitude of trust. An attitude which helps those who toil through even the most difficult of circumstances to realize that the tears of pilgrims are never permanent.

We find our hero where all who desire to walk the high road of the calling of Christ will often find themselves: facing closed doors. These are the seasons of our life when we have to go through what wise people of ancient times have described as "the dark night of the soul." We will be wise to notice that saints of all ages have talked about this way of God with His children to allow them to go through seasons of dryness:

Sometimes you shall find yourself so absolutely destitute of all feeling of devotion that your soul shall seem to be a wild, fruitless, barren desert, in which there is no trace of a pathway to find her God, nor any water of grace to refresh her, on account of dryness which seems to threaten her with a total and absolute desolation.

Francis de Sales

Notice in our story how there seems to be depths of despair even fiercer than we feel we can bear. Some doors of life seem to be so inexplicably and permanently locked that every answer we have ever had does not seem to make sense anymore. Such is the darkness we will learn about in our story.

During these seasons of shadow no superficial slogans of feel-good seminars or self-help best-sellers will help us.

It is better to see the truth and accept that in some trials of life only utter surrender and the acknowledgement that we have reached the end of all the powers of our being, will do.

The dark night of the soul will lead us on to what seems to be the darkest and most forsaken deserts man can enter. And yet, these are also the holiest of places a pilgrim can arrive at on the journey of the spirit.

Only those who have arrived where the Great Champion of our faith once was, will know the holiness of forsaken places. Here we find not flashy praises and instant joy, but we hear the words that cause the gates of hell to tremble:

My God, my God, why hast thou forsaken me?

Notice how the hero of our story did not find this dark place to be completely strange. And so it is with us also. The great battles of life are not completely new. They tend to repeat our earlier battles, only they are more intense. It will not do, therefore, to think that one day, when the great battles of life do come, we will fight with the required courage.

The battle is always now. Small battles today prepare us for greater battles tomorrow. Such is the warning of the prophet of old:

If thou hast run with the footmen, and they have wearied thee, then how canst thou contend with horses?

JEREMIAH 12:5

We can learn from wise men of old that seasons of doubt and despair need not harm us, but may even help us to walk in the footsteps of Him who was most forsaken of all.

Many have walked this lonely road and all of them speak with gratitude of Him who granted them the grace to visit where He Himself, the Holy One, had been. He not only knows the way there, but He knows the way through all valleys. In His footsteps we will learn, as our hero has, that for those on the right way there is no night that lasts forever:

I have plumbed the depths of despair
and have found them not bottomless.
Thomas Hardy

And on our quest we will be changed, often more by the tough times than the good times. As if through shadows we get to the light.

Despair can be the Gate of Dawn
And Death itself but Heaven's Door

And so our story will lead us to learn that all who would go on to higher places will sometimes stand in front of the closed doors of the palaces of destiny. We may hammer on them with rocks of desperation. We may try to enter through iron-barred windows, or be hurt in our endeavors to find other entrances. All of us will enter the dark night of the soul.

Not one of us will be immune from failure, doubt, or great sadness. But still, there will always be only one door for every palace and only one key for every door, and if we can see beauty, even in the darkness of life, that key will be beckoning.

From ancient wisdom we learn that hidden keys of mysterious palaces will be found only by those who have come through the darkness and have proceeded to become the conquerors of life's Peaks of Great Challenge. As we go again to the ancient times of our simple story, notice the inner strength of our hero of the mountains and decide to become a conqueror of high peaks.

Seven Strengths of the Conquerors of High Peaks

1. Conquerors of High Peaks have deep desires.
   If you have no desire, desire more than anything to desire.

2. Conquerors of High Peaks know failure.
   How will I succeed, father?
   Learn to fail, my son.

3. Conquerors of High Peaks find new desire from moments of surrender.
   Oh, bitter death of surrender. Oh, sweet life of surrender.

4. Conquerors of High Peaks make decisions with great determination.
   "I have succeeded" must always be preceded by "I have decided" and both these by "... even if I fail".

5. Conquerors of High Peaks are willing to travel without anyone to where no one has been.
   Oh, sweet solitude, if not for thy fair company, how lonely I would be.

6. Conquerors of High Peaks know that without taking the next step, the peak will never be reached.

Tomorrow has the flavor of dreams, yesterday the flavor of wisdom, but only today has the sweet smell of life.

7. Conquerors of High Peaks will climb until their last day.

When you die, may it not be before you have lived.

Mark the commitment of The Owner of the House of Many Colors to go on his quest regardless of the cost. Without such commitment no mountain peak can be conquered.

W. H. Murray, leader of the Scottish expedition to the Himalayas, was asked what the secret of their success on that treacherous mission was. His answer will serve as an inspiration to all of us on the dangerous journey of life:

Until one is committed, there is hesitancy, the chance to draw back. Concerning all acts of initiative and creation there is one elementary truth, the ignorance which kills countless ideas and splendid plans: that moment one definitely commits oneself, providence moves too. All sorts of things occur to help one that would never otherwise have occurred.

A whole stream of events issues from the decision, raising in one's favor all manner of unforseen incidents and meetings and material assistance, which no man could have dreamed would come his way.

I have learned a deep respect for one of Goethe's couplets:

> *Whatever you can do or dream you can, begin it.*
> *Boldness has genius, power and magic in it.*

I would not consider any spirituality worthwhile that wants to walk in sweetness and ease and run from the imitation of Christ.
John Climacus

towards high peaks
and hidden keys

THE OWNER OF the House of Many Colors walked around the palace and found only one entrance to it.

He stood in front of it, and there, engraved with ancient letters on the majestic, big front door, were the words: "The Palace of Royalty Beyond and Within – Abode of their Majesties, Kings and Queens of Humanity from The Great City Potential."

For a while, the fear that had come upon him with the ominous silence was becoming even more intense.

Should he enter or should he not? Why was there no one around?

He remembered that he had read in one of the ancient books in his library, *The Book of Separation*, of the punishment for those who entered palaces without permission. He wondered if following the council members down the mountain would not be the wise thing to do. Was this not maybe a place of doom and curses? It felt to him as if there was a battle raging in his mind. A part of him wanted only for things to return to normal, but another part of him was feeling the call to destined things.

In the battle raging in his mind there was something familiar. He remembered how he had been feeling all the years in The Town called Potential. He remembered the many instances when he had to make difficult choices and they were never in agreement with the opinions of the town council.

Now, although the intensity of the battle in his mind was greater, it was not different. He could not now, after all those years of following his heart and listening to those inner convictions that were mostly unpopular, choose the way down the mountain – he had always dreamt of higher ground. And all the while he was hearing in his mind the words in the breath of the strong wind; *Come to find your destiny, come to find your destiny ...*

He could not forget those words. They seemed to have an increasing power over him. Although the fear would not go away, the words in his mind began to get the upper hand. And it seemed to him that this was the way that it had always been with him. Fear had never been quite absent from his heart, but he had always believed the wisdom of the ancient books that it is futile to try and conquer fear by waiting for it to go away.

Patience, such was the teaching of ancient wisdom, although being a great virtue, would not by its own power conquer fear. Patience could easily turn into indecision in the absence of courage. The courageous are not those who have no fear, but those who choose to believe that in spite of dreadful possibilities, it is worthwhile to pursue noble deeds.

And so he decided to believe that he was once again at the crossroads of destiny. Although he was still afraid, he knew that in this, The Palace of Royalty Beyond and Within – Abode of their Majesties, Kings and Queens of Humanity from The Great City Potential, he would find his destiny. Inside him was a burning desire to enter those ancient doors and a sense of mystery, danger, fear, joy and courage – in short he felt alive. It was time for action. Surely, success was close at hand …

He tried to open the door, but either it was locked, or it had been out of use for so long that the hinges had become rusted. He struggled all day, banging on the door with rocks and logs, but he could not open it.

He even climbed up the wall of the palace to one of the high windows, but it had thick iron bars in front of it. He climbed further up to see if he could not enter through the roof, but halfway up, built into the wall, were sharp blades that cut him as he desperately tried to climb higher. With painful, bleeding wounds, he realized that it was impossible to reach the palace roof, and with an even braver effort he climbed down the wall again.

Back in front of the closed door, The Owner of the House of Many Colors was staring at the palace. The feeling that came over him was one that he was not familiar with. His heart sank into the deepest valley of disappointment and he felt like a worthless failure.

Questions in his mind made him feel as if he was immersed in a dark cloud of doom. Was all this effort worth it? Was it worth believing in the beauty of life for so many years? He remembered the rejection and scorn of the people in The Town called Potential. Why had he not chosen the easy road? Was it not time to give up on his dreams and just be a normal person, living in an ordinary gray house? Were all the ancient books of wisdom not merely worthless information from outdated and ignorant sources? Were the people in their gray houses with their gray library not right after all?

It went on for hours. As the night became dark and cold, it seemed as if the darkness was tormenting his soul. He cried bitter tears and shouted at the sky. Who was the cruel one who would show him the palace of his dreams and then let him lie bleeding in front of a closed door? Was this the twisted purpose of the one determining his destiny? And all the while the feeling of utter loneliness, utter failure. For the first time in his life he tasted the bitter taste of failure in the dark night of the soul.

As if triumphant, the palace was glowing as the moonlight played on the impenetrable door and walls. It looked even bigger now. He felt only a sad and faint desire to see what was behind those ancient walls.

The tired Owner of The House of Many Colors felt like the night would never end as he was lying there in the dark shadow of the palace. He searched his mind for words of hope from the ancient books of wisdom, but even the ancient words now seemed meaningless and empty.

There was nowhere to turn to for hope and courage. This seemed to be in contradiction of everything he had ever believed. All his dreams had been just that – dreams; the illusions of a fanciful idiot. The people of The Town called Potential had after all been right, he was The Strange One, he was a fool.

In discouragement he fell to the ground and just stared into the cold and empty night.

But no night is really empty.

How long he had been lying there and just when he first noticed that the night was in fact not empty, he did not know. How could he not have seen the stars, the moon, and the peaceful softness of faraway clouds? Where had the night sounds suddenly come from? A while ago everything seemed so deadly quiet, but suddenly he realized that the night was filled with sounds of life.

Gazing at the stars and seeing the beauty of those ancient skies, it seemed as if the great beauty above him slowly began penetrating his mind and replacing the darkness inside. Beauty was a reality.

It dawned on him that even if he would never be able to see what was inside the palace, there would still be stars and mountains, rivers and oceans, birds and flowers and trees.

In his heart he surrendered. If the palace door was impenetrable, he would accept it, but he would not give up on life. The stars were shining and he realized that they were higher than any palace, and more beautiful.

The dark night of the soul was gone.

Then, suddenly, while beholding the beauty around and above him, he felt again that old familiar spark of desire. Strangely, having given up all hope of opening the palace door, the desire to see what was beyond those ancient walls was back now, stronger than ever.

While it was true that during that very same night he had felt that he had lost all faith in the ancient words of wisdom, he now could think of nothing else. Words he had been planting in the soil of his heart through the years now proved to be rooted deeper than he thought. They would not even be removed by this fierce battle of the soul.

Like food for the hungry, water for the thirsty and remedy for the afflicted, these words seemed to him to be restoring his body and soul. Courage returned to his heart as he pondered on old stories of kings and mountains, good and bad dragons, great battles and unwavering bravery.

And then he remembered something written in *The Book of Separation* in the chapter called *Wisdom Concerning Travels to Places of Great Desiny:* "The Greater the challenge, the greater the need for resolution. The Palace prepared for Many, Chosen by Few, who can open its formidable door, if not he who would climb the highest peak; The Peak of Great Resolution, and brave the deepest cave; The Cave of the Fiercest Dragon met by too few?"

Could it be that the key to The Palace of Royalty Beyond and Within – Abode of their Majesties, Kings and Queens of Humanity from The Great City Potential was kept in a cave on The Peak of Great Challenge? Was The Peak of Great Resolution not maybe another name for, but exactly the same place as The Peak of Great Challenge? A night of questions now suddenly seemed to be turning into a night that provided the one answer he had been looking for.

And that night he decided that he would be the first man from The Town called Potential to put his feet on the highest peak of all and, if destined, meet the Fiercest of all dragons, which was also called The Hungry Dragon in some ancient literature. It was not just a whim. Neither was it a decision that was made with any reservations. He was not merely going to investigate. His decision would not be dependent on what he would find on the way. Yes, the thought of The Hungry Dragon made him tremble with fear, but even so, he was abandoning himself on a mission with his heart prepared to give whatever it would take.

Many times the next day The Owner of the House of Many Colors knew why the people of The Town called Potential referred to the mountain as Mount Impossibility. Many times he wished for another one of those strange storms that had taken him and the other men to the higher regions of the mountain. This was, of course, only a wish, since he was wise enough to know that most storms come when one does not expect them, not when one wishes for them.

The clouds were dense and dark and almost alive. It felt as if they were challenging him to push through them. Now and then it sounded as if they were thundering, he could not decide whether in laughter or in warning. Were they mocking or encouraging?

He climbed all day without knowing how far he was from the top. All he could see was the next step, but in his mind he could hear the words, *Come to find your destiny*, and he had visions of an open palace door. Suffering and persevering, he learned that The Peak of Great Challenge was indeed The Peak of Great Resolution.

The moment came when he had no strength left. His tired and aching body was crying out and in his mind the desire to lie down and accept his fate of dying alone without ever entering the palace, was making every step a new battle, even against himself.

He knew that this was the end, but would rather die plunging down to the waiting rocks of Mount Royal than give up. He cried his last tears and waited for his last moments as his legs would finally lose the battle of the next step.

But then, after many hours of dark clouds around him, suddenly, in one moment, there was sunshine,

sunshine so bright that it seemed as if there had never been clouds on Mount Royal. He could see what no one from The Town called Potential had ever seen. Mount Impossibility was actually Mount Possibility and he was standing on top of the world.

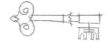

Chapter 6

Of Servants, Leaders and Compromise

Be sober, be vigilant; because your adversary the devil, as a roaring lion, walketh about, seeking whom he may devour.

1 Peter 5:8

THE WARNING IS clear. The enemy is real and the enemy is dangerous. But the enemy is also subtle. He destroys when we least expect it.

Many have been his victims who thought that things were well with them when in fact, the enemy was at hand and his work had been in progress for many a season of oblivion.

They were at the very threshold of darkness while thinking they were in the light. But the limelight is not to be mistaken for the light.

There is a saying, *He who does business with death will soon be in head office.* The sad thing is that very few really know the deceptions of him who Jesus called "a murderer from the beginning" (cf. John 8:44). What is the essence of his evil?

The lives of those pathetic souls whom we have met in our story, the members of the town council of The Town called Potential, will serve as a reminder to us that the essence of evil is pride. Pride kills. It kills by deceiving people into thinking that they have life within themselves, they are independent and self-existent.

Theirs are the opinions that matter. Theirs are the virtues to be admired. Theirs (if indeed there is still room for more than one self) is the inner circle which alone has significance. And so, caught in the trap of self-worship, they remove themselves from the only Source of Life.

We are reminded by a wise man that all the weapons of the Evil One have the same poison:

Pride.
The essential vice, the utmost evil,
is Pride ... Pride leads to every other vice:
it is the complete anti-God state of mind.
C. S. Lewis

Mark, as we consider everything that happens in the gray town, how life brings the opportunities for us to conquer pride. We do not discern these graces. They come and we view them as enemies. Because pride makes it hard for us to bow, we are agitated by any call to service.

Service becomes to us the one threat to those things which have set themselves up like despots in our souls; the desire to feel important, to be above others and to be soothed by the thought of our own greatness. We view service as the enemy, when in fact, as Richard Foster remarks, it is the one friend we desperately need:

More than any other single way,
the grace of humility is worked into our lives
through the discipline of service ... Nothing disciplines
the inordinate desires of the flesh like service ...

Let not those who are still within the reach of the call to bow and serve, underestimate the urgency of the call. During the whole of life's journey there is the battle for our soul.

The Enemy of Man would not have us suspect that the battle is indeed between an Evil One and the God who is only good. His ways are more subtle. We are deceived into thinking that we are involved in the struggle of reaching our potential.

Our focus is on our own purposes. We fear total commitment to God. In the same way as those who heard the ancient whispers of a serpent in a garden, we fear that bowing without reserve or condition will make us poorer, steal from us whatever greatness or joy life has to offer.

Deep within us we have the good desire to bow and serve, but also the evil ambition to make it on our own. To our own detriment will we live lives of compromise and bow halfway only, for in time we will surely altogether refuse to bow:

> Woe to those weak and timid souls
> who are divided between God and their world!
> They want and they do not want.
> They are torn by desire and remorse at the same time...
> They have a horror of evil and a shame of good.

They have the pains of virtue without tasting its sweet
consolations. O how wretched they are.
Francois Fénelon

Those who refuse to heed the ever-present call of
Service will in time go beyond the reach of her beautiful
voice. Caught up in the cruel entanglement of the
incessant prideful cravings of the self, their eyes will
have turned away from all others to only the desires of
the inward fool who wishes alone to be served as king,
blind to the sad truth that he has long since become a
slave in eternal chains.

A damned soul is nearly nothing: it is shrunk,
shut up in itself. Good beats upon the damned incessantly
as sound waves beat on the ears of the deaf,
but they cannot receive it. Their fists are clenched,
their eyes fast shut. First they will not,
in the end they cannot, open their hands for gifts,
or their mouths for food, or their eyes to see.
C. S. Lewis

cruel dragons and
dangerous friends

BACK IN THE Town called Potential, the people had finally come to the point of realizing that something would have to be done about the nightly visitations of the cruel monster. Some even started suggesting that the monster could well be Dragon Mediocrity. Somehow the dreadful circumstances they had been experiencing lately had brought about a change in their way of thinking. There seemed to be many opinions and discussions and even letters being circulated insisting on a crisis meeting of the town council. The general consensus was that it was time for action.

The members of the town council were very much opposed to the opinion that it was time for action. They were also very disturbed by what was becoming the popular opinion, namely that Mediocrity could well be the cruel monster.

They could, however, not put the matter on the agenda of an official council meeting (which was not due soon in any case), since all council meetings were attended by the other inhabitants of the town and this meeting would certainly be no different. It clearly seemed that there would be serious differences of opinion and, of course, the rules for council meetings did not make allowance for differences of opinion.

It was also unacceptable that the ordinary citizens would call for a meeting of the town council. Where were things going to end if anyone could just insist on such meetings? There were procedures to be followed and rules to be kept.

Now, more than ever, it was a time to trust the leaders. Already their way of life had changed so drastically, why now change their tried and trusted traditions and conventions?

These arguments would normally be quite sufficient to convince the people, but this time they kept insisting on having a meeting, and, somehow, there was a look in the eyes of the people, a tone in their voice, that made the council members realize that their own safety, security and stability might well be in jeopardy. It seemed clear that a meeting there was going to be, with or without the council members. So, the council announced that there would be a special and extraordinary meeting in the town hall.

In the meeting the council made it clear that rules were rules, and that it was still against the rules of proper governance that there may be differences of opinion in a council meeting. The people were reminded of how upsetting and deeply disturbing it had been when on a previous occasion, a certain strange citizen had for the first time in history differed from the council. And had things not been deteriorating ever since?

The poor townsfolk were suddenly feeling that old familiar feeling that important matters should maybe be left to be handled by these trusted leaders. Maybe ordinary people like themselves were unable to understand these weighty matters.

The council members were very satisfied with the direction in which the meeting was going and promptly announced that the rest of the meeting would be for informational and explanatory purposes only. How good it felt to have control again.

The council felt it was their duty to remind the

people that they, as council members, had gone up into the middle regions of the mountain on water-fetching duties without any encounters with Dragon Mediocrity. They explained that this was sufficient proof that Mediocrity could not be their cruel nightly visitor and that the monster definitely came from another region in the mountain.

Just as the people started feeling at ease and ready to accept a motion of confidence in the town council, somebody broke the accepted rules of council meetings for the second time in the history of The Town called Potential.

Since The Owner of the House of Many Colors had not yet returned from the mountain, his family was attending the meeting. Because they had never before attended such a meeting, and had never been interested in the rules and customs of council meetings, they were not even aware that they were now breaking these rules and customs. These rules and customs, as we already know, were of course that nobody was allowed to raise his voice above the customary and civilized level of seriousness; nobody interrupted the speaker with any remarks; nobody made any humorous impromptu comments; nobody differed from the previous speaker, but only added comments to confirm the argument and, most importantly, nobody asked any questions.

The Strange Ones had some interesting views. These views were clearly influenced by their study of the ancient books of wisdom, but they wisely did not mention it. They asked very simple questions in the meeting (although many people thought these were ingenious questions, and could not think why nobody had thought of such deep and profound things before). Their questions made the members of the council feel very uncomfortable. Some of the questions were recorded in the ancient history of The Town called Potential:

- If you keep handling the problem as you have been doing, what will it eventually lead to?
- Do you have all the available facts or do you regard untested opinions as facts?
- Do you have a plan?
- Who will implement the plan, and when?

Even The Strange Ones were surprised when there were serious nods of approval all around. Only the members of the council thought that these were outrageous questions, inspired by ideas that were totally contrary to the town council's way of thinking. The members of the council were, however, not the kind of people who were used to disagreeing with the majority and it was not long before they joined in, seriously nodding in approval.

This approval from the town council was met with more approval again from the people for their very intelligent and open-minded council. They immediately proceeded with a unanimous vote of confidence, which the members of the council each humbly accepted, with speeches, not forgetting to thank their wives too.

Unprecedented enthusiasm was experienced as there were cheers from the people. It was clear that the stress of the nightly visits of the monster was having an effect on their emotions and some were even shedding thankful tears, because something was finally going to be done about their dreadful situation.

In this spirit of confidence, one of those who attended the meeting proposed that there could be no other persons more worthy of the honorable task of getting the facts, constructing a plan and overseeing its implementation, than their honorable council. Since the monster had not visited for a while, and was expected to do so soon, he also proposed that the honorable members of the council should, that very day, depart to hide out in the mountain until the next visit of the monster.

Theirs should be the noble task to find out the truth about who the dragon really was. Only the council members could be entrusted with such an important responsibility and only they would be able to proceed with the making of a plan to end the monster's reign of terror. Who else, but the worthy council members, could be called upon at times like these to be the servants of their community.

The members of the council shuddered as they heard the words "truth," "facts," "plans" and "responsibility." Somehow, they longed to hear the words they had always regarded as words worthy of the attention of council members – words like "convention," "procedure" and "tradition."

Also ominously absent were words like "seniority," "popularity" and "position". What about old favorites like "status quo," "unity" and "custom?"

Worst of all was the frequent use of a word they had never been fond of at all, a word they had always regarded as an insult – after all, were they not leaders, how could anyone refer to them as servants! The very idea was preposterous, to say the least.

Furthermore, what was all the fuss about action? Surely it was grossly unfair to expect from them as honorable council members to engage in any real action. Were they not to oversee meetings and engage in deep thought and discussion? How could they attend to vulgar things such as being involved in dangerous life-saving missions?

It has to be noted that it went by quite unnoticed that history was again in the making since with all these

protests there was no regard for rules concerning in-
terrupting previous speakers, the raising of voices and
asking of questions.

It was the very first time that the custodians of these
rules and traditions showed no regard for them at all.
In their defense it could be argued that the rules at this
specific occasion seemed to be in conflict with the safety,
security and stability of the council members.

One could say that the protests of the council members were passionate, which in itself was something
very unusual, but even so, they could not succeed in pas-
sifying the crowd.

For the fourth time in history, the accepted rules for
council meetings were broken, as the members of the
council were politely interrupted and unanimously
praised by the rest of the people.

The almost wonderful, vaguely beautiful, very nearly
ingenious and definitely (although not really aware of
it) very precious people of The Town called Potential
saw these protests as a most commendable sign of the
humility of their beloved councilors and once again
there were serious, almost jubilant nods of approval
throughout the room.

The protesting councilors were, without further ado,
carried out to the foot of Mount Royal on the shoulders
of the appreciative crowd. By late afternoon they arrived

at the mountain but the crowd would not return home until they had seen the brave councilors disappear into the forest in the middle regions of the mountain. The sun disappeared and blue skies made way for the beautiful colors of a day gone by and eventually the darkness of an unknown night fell.

It may be worth mentioning that the councilors would probably have refused to go into the mountain forest, had it not been that the appreciative crowd seemed determined to not let the council members refuse the honor of being the heroes they had been hailed as being. They were determined not only in an enthusiastic, but in almost a strangely violent sort of way …

The fear of the councilors was indescribable, but for reasons that the people were unaware of. On their journey into the mountain with The Owner of the House of Many Colors, he had spoken to them at length about various important subjects.

He knew that they would not remain on the mountain with him, but hoped that they would return to The Town called Potential with new insight. He warned them that they had a very important responsibility and gave them two documents and begged them to read them. The first he copied from a book called *The Ancient Guide for Kings and Rulers*.

Three Deadly Follies of Foolish Rulers:

1. **Foolish rulers love comfort and avoid reality.**
   "He who turns his back on the facts will face the consequences."

2. **Foolish rulers love external applause and avoid internal conviction.**
   "He who always swims with the tide will drown in Lake Popularity."

3. **Foolish rulers love important positions and avoid important responsibilities.**
   "Pity him who would be called maestro, but performs when he should be practising, and when performing sounds like he is practising."

They did read this first document and the only comment that can be made about their reaction is that they were deeply offended.

The second document came from his latest studies on dragons. He had spent nights and nights in order to get information that would help him protect the people of The Town called Potential. His findings were startling and called for immediate action. Of course it would be required of the council members to mobilize the townsfolk and begin with an immediate protection plan. This should be followed by a plan of attack against at least Dragon Mediocrity, if not against more of his kind.

Upon returning to town, they thought it wise not to take immediate action, but to take some time in giving thought to the so-called findings of The Owner of the House of Many Colors. They did not regard this as procrastination, but rather as wisdom.

The Owner of the House of Many Colors had warned them that there was no time to waste, but he was in their view of obvious fanatic inclination and his views could not be taken too seriously.

But now, in the darkness and chill of the ominously quiet night, all they could think of was the document that The Owner of the House of Many Colors had given them. In fact, one of the councilors had it with him. Somehow they knew that what was written in it would make this night darker than any other night.

They wished that they had followed the advice of The Owner of the House of Many Colors. Ironically, what should have saved them, now had a dreadful message. What could have helped them, now made them feel more doomed. They had with them a list of dangerous dragons against which the books of ancient wisdom had warned all people:

Ancient Index of the
Brotherhood of Evil Dragons.

Three Ruling Dragons Most Feared, with Friends:

1. **The Great Dragon of Evil: Pride**
   Two Faithful Friends:
   The Unyielding Dragons: Humiliation and Loneliness

2. **The Mighty Dragon: Covetousness**
   Two Faithful Friends:
   The Relentless Dragons: Unsatisfied and Poverty

3. **The Strong Dragon: Lust**
   Two Faithful Friends:
   The Cruel Dragons: MoreLust and LessLove

Eight Dragons with Friends to be Underestimated at your Peril:

1. Dragon Ease, with Friends, Boredom and Weakness
2. Dragon Procrastination, with Friends, Crisis and Cancellation
3. Dragon Fear, with Friends, Pessimism and Decay
4. Dragon Grudge, with Friends, Resentment and Alienation
5. Dragon Half-Truth, with Friends, No-Truth and Deceit
6. Dragon Know-All, with Friends, Pig-Head and Presumption
7. Dragon Two-Face, with Friends, No-Face and Shame
8. Dragon Compromise, with Friends, Mediocrity and Insignificance.

The members of the town council could think of nothing but how afraid they were, nothing else, not even having a council meeting. After minutes that felt like ages, the deadening silence was broken by the even more deadening sound of the roar of a monster. The monster clearly had only one intention and that was to get to The Town called Potential.

The councilors would have seen this, had they only stuck to their task of finding out what monster it was, but they were overcome by fear and fled for their lives to a part of the mountain completely unknown to them.

They would never know it, but they had been so very close to becoming real heroes …

As they heard the roars of the monster disappear into the distance, the members of the town council felt the welcome reassurance of safety for the first time that night – why, if the dragon would kill another one or two of the townsfolk that night, then that was just too bad. At least they, the leaders, the important members of the council, were safe, why should they be worrying about ordinary, unimportant people?

And then, suddenly, the earth seemed to shake beneath them as they heard a roar so ferocious that its message could mean nothing but death.

Before seeing the eyes of evil and feeling the teeth inside the jaws of a monster more cruel and gigantic than they could ever have imagined, they had time only to see a name-tag similiar to the one around the neck of their favorite little dragon. But the name was one they did not know.

These were the last words they would ever read, the name of a dragon whose existence they had been oblivious of:

Compromise: Killer of the Half-hearted, Eternal Friend of the Great and Unmerciful Dragon Mediocrity and the Important Dragon Insignificance.

Chapter 7

Of Progress and Caring

I have learned, in whatsoever state I am, therewith to be content. I know both how to be abased, and I know how to abound: every where and in all things I am instructed both to be full and to be hungry, both to abound and to suffer need. I can do all things through Christ which strengtheneth me.

PHILIPPIANS 4:11-13

THE WORDS *"I can do all things through Christ which strengtheneth me,"* must surely be some of the most frequently quoted words of the Bible, and maybe also some of the most wrongly quoted words of the Bible. People use this verse to affirm their belief that they can achieve great things. This is their success slogan, their prosperity puntline.

Paul does not say that the strength of Christ has given him only success and prosperity. In fact, he suggests that he has also learned about failure and in this instance he refers to the failure of ensuring enduring financial stability.

Elsewhere he also mentions failure to ensure success in his ministry, or to arrive at planned destinations, or to get his physical health to a desired state. It even seems at one stage that he may not have been quite blameless in his handling of the disagreement between himself and Barnabas (cf. Acts 15:36-41).

So, far from stating that he enjoys permanent victory, Paul rather suggests that through all the seasons of life, with all its joys and victories, its prosperity and abundance, but also with its problems and defeat, despite all his own weaknesses, the presence of Christ has helped him to persevere in his walk of faith.

Seeing that this great apostle of faith experienced times of weakness will help us not to be side-tracked by an idealistic expectation that our faith in Christ and devotion to Him will prevent defeat and weakness in our lives. In fact, Paul teaches us that in his experience of difficulty he learned that God inspires us not only in spite of our weaknesses and inabilities, but often because of them.

Paul arrived at a place where, instead of preaching perfectionism, he rejoiced in the reality of his struggles. He was gently taught and encouraged by the Holy Spirit, that great Guide and Friend of all people who want to have a better understanding of their weaknesses.

Out of Paul's struggle to come to terms with his own weaknesses came words that have aided many a pilgrim on his journey when struggles have threatened to overburden him:

And he said unto me, my grace is sufficient for thee: for my power is made perfect in weakness. Most gladly therefore will I rather glory in my infirmities, that the power of Christ may rest upon me. Therefore I take pleasure in infirmities, in reproaches, in necessities, in persecutions, in distresses, for Christ's sake: for when I am weak, then am I strong.

2 CORINTHIANS 12:9-10

This reality, that our experience of weakness makes available God's strength, is one of those principles of

God's rulership that seems so at odds with our under-standing of life.

As we continue in our story of the journey of him they called The Strange One, we are reminded of this strangeness. Our hero experiences timidity, not realizing that there is power in timidity, and also timidity in all true power. We often think that we are weak, when in fact we are greatly growing in strength, or in the words of St. John of the Cross: "In general, the soul makes greater progress when it least thinks so ... most frequently when it imagines that it is losing."

This sense of weakness and timidity accomplishes two great things in us. Firstly, it gives us a deep sense of dependence on God. It takes us to our Source, and there we draw upon His strength and become qualified to do those great things which only He can help us do. Jesus taught His disciples that there is no other way than this way of dependence:

Abide in me, and I in you. As the branch cannot bear fruit of itself, except it abide in the vine; no more can ye, except ye abide in me. I am the vine, ye are the branches: He that abideth in me, and I in him, the same bringeth forth much fruit: for apart from me ye can do nothing.

JOHN 15:4-5

Secondly, we are so aware of our own inability to do great things, that we are willing to regard ourselves as qualified only to serve others. In our timidity, we are saved from our self-importance and feel at ease only by being servants. God's strange, but ingenious plan to install His own greatness in us is now at work. We are becoming like the greatest Servant who ever walked the earth.

> *Let nothing be done through selfish ambition or conceit, but in lowliness of mind let each esteem others better than himself. Let each of you look out not only for his own interests, but also for the interests of others. Let this mind be in you which was also in Christ Jesus, who, being in the form of God, did not consider it robbery to be equal with God, but made Himself of no reputation, taking the form of a bondservant.*
>
> PHILIPPIANS 2:3-7, (NKJV)

We join our hero again on the mountain and find him in this spirit, not obsessed only with his own dreams, but deeply committed to help those who are living as if blindfolded. We sense that his quest is ours also, a quest to become like Him who deeply cared about the souls of all who are in this tragic state, and we are reminded of the words of a great man of wisdom:

Nothing can be more cruel than the leniency
which abandons others to their sin. Nothing can be
more compassionate than the severe reprimand
which calls another ... back from the path of sin.
Dietrich Bonhoeffer

names forgotten and
names revealed

THE VIEW FROM the highest peak of Mount Possibility was breathtakingly beautiful. As far as the eye could see were hills and valleys, streams and lakes and it seemed like someone had decided to paint a picture with as many colors as he could find. Every green had a thousand shades, as did every red, yellow, brown and blue and countless other colors, which were unknown to The Owner of the House of Many Colors. It was as if the earth was singing a song in praise of beauty.

But there was a place that did not seem to be joining in the song of praise; The Town called Potential. One could almost hear the out-of-tune and monotonous lament as its one shade of gray rebelled against the beauty surrounding it. Only one house with a certain colorful library, filled with ancient books of wisdom, were in harmony with the celebration of life at the foot of Mount Possibility.

Looking down at the dull, gray town, The Owner of the House of Many Colors was filled with sadness and great pity. He knew that if something wasn't done, all those almost wonderful, vaguely beautiful, very nearly ingenious and definitely very precious people in The Town called Potential would certainly not be alive for very much longer. He knew that he had to find the key to The Palace of Royalty Beyond and Within – Abode of their Majesties, Kings and Queens of Humanity from The Great City Potential if he was to help them at all.

Having quenched his thirst with ice cold water from a crystal clear stream, he suddenly felt as if he had never been tired. He felt magically rejuvenated and started exploring. He was quite sure by now that The Peak of Great Challenge and The Peak of Great Resolution were indeed one and the same place. He was searching for a hidden cave, where he was sure he would find the key to The Palace prepared for Many, Chosen by Few. By now

The Owner of the House of Many Colors felt as if he had not only read *The Book Of Separation*, but was indeed part of it, living it. He had no doubt that there was a place called the Palace prepared for Many, Chosen by Few, which had doors that had to be opened ...

The wind on top of the mountain was blowing just strong enough to make some whispering and moaning sounds. These sounds made The Owner of the House of Many Colors somewhat uneasy. It almost sounded like heavy breathing. He tried to convince himself that it was the wind, but the moaning and breathing seemed to be coming from an opening in a huge rock, some distance away.

The closer he got to the opening, the louder and more distinctive the breathing became. By now the breathing sounded much more like roaring and his uneasiness felt much more like fear.

As he approached the opening, he found that it was a very big entrance to the biggest cave he had ever seen. It was also very different from caves he was used to. Everything was impeccably neat. Nothing was out of place. It even felt as if the air inside the cave was fresher than the air outside. There were hundreds of ancient books, many of which The Owner of the House of Many Colors was very familiar with.

In fact, the cave reminded him of his very own library,

but also of the palace. There was not a trace of darkness, everything was as colorful as the palace and in a way also as his own house which now felt to be a lifetime away.

He was still amazed at how these colors of beauty had been with him all his life when he realized that the roaring, breathing, moaning sounds had become quiet. For a moment The Owner of the House of Many Colors felt relieved at the thought that it had after all only been the howling of the wind, which, aided by his fear and imagination, made him think of big animals and monsters.

The moment of relief did not last very long. As his eyes were getting used to the brilliant light in the cave, he felt in every raised hair and every drop of sweat trickling down his forehead and his back the terrible sensation of being completely overtaken by fear.

"I have waited a long time for you to come," sounded the deepest and most frightening voice he had ever heard.

He could only tremble. Speaking was impossible. Everything within him wanted to flee, and yet, at the same time, everything within him wanted to stay and meet the one with the deep and frightening voice.

"Fear can be the good thing that makes you a hero or the bad thing that makes you a coward. I see that it has been a good thing to you," said the voice. "Come closer then, Brave One."

He took one tentative step and then stared into the eyes of a dragon as big and awesome as the biggest dragons written about in the ancient books of wisdom. The eyes of the dragon were fierce and fiery, but also very beautiful.

The Owner of the House of Many Colors was desperately afraid of the creature in front of him, even looking at it filled him with dread and trepidation. He trembled and swallowed. He froze and felt his heart beating so violently that he was sure the dragon could see his chest throbbing. His mouth was dry and he knew he was in the presence of danger such as he had never known. This was surely one of the greatest foes a man could meet.

Our poor hero could not understand what was happening inside him. He had never seen the dragon before, but felt as if he had always known it very well. It surely was a stranger, but it also felt as if it was his closest friend. He felt threatened and yet at home; very much alive, but desperately close to the end of his life. This was beauty – he could not stop staring in wonder – yet he could not stand looking at it. It was the kind of beauty that hurts. This was mystery with all its awe-inspiring invitation, but with the unmistakable warning of deep and eternal danger.

"What is your name?" The voice was deep, frightening and lovely.

"I have a dreaded name. Some ancient books make mention of it, but it is hard for me to understand its meaning. I have never been called by this name. My people call me The Strange One, or The Owner of the House of Many Colors." He thought that his voice sounded very timid and frightened, and he was quite correct.

"Blessed is he who is called The Strange One by those whose barren hearts have never tasted the power of beauty, wisdom or courage. Blessed he who has a house of many colors in the gray world of conformity. And did you know that the dreaded name can be both inherited or chosen and that those who choose it will discover the way of life?"

"I have read as much in the ancient books, but have never understood."

"Soon you will," said the dragon and once again The Owner of the House of Many Colors was torn between great anxiety and great excitement and longing. He long-ed to know more about the dreaded name, but he also felt that he would rather never learn anything about it. There must be a reason why people have for so long avoided it. What was in that name?

Suddenly he remembered that he was on the mountain to look for the key to the palace. For a moment he stopped thinking of names and mysteries and colors and palaces, and his heart felt again the pain and sadness at the thought of those poor souls obsessed with their wretched safety, security and stabilty.

He thought of their stifled life, their gray existence and he desired more than he could express to bring them to these worlds of color, of mountain air and life. Their poor, gray little valley which they regarded as a haven, a defense, was indeed a prison. If only they could see what was beyond their tiny world. If only they could even feel the thrill of being in the presence of danger. Then somehow he mustered enough courage to speak to the dragon of his own accord.

"Mister Dragon, sir ..."

"You can call me by my name," said the dragon, and The Owner of the House of Many Colors correctly understood this to be a command and not a suggestion.

"Excuse me, sir, but I do not know your name."

"Oh, but you do, Brave One."

Fear gripped his pounding heart again, as he searched his racing mind for a name he thought he had rudely and carelessly forgotten. He expected the wrath of the dragon at any moment.

"My name has been with you for a long time. My name is in the heart before it is in the mind. My name is a passion before it is knowledge. My name is like yours, a dreaded name. Yet, those who get aquainted with it will grow to love it. Those who use it often will wish to use it all the more. And you have used it often, you have been wise."

Once again The Owner of the House of Many Colors was convinced that there was some kind of mistake. He had no idea what the great dragon was talking about. Still, he almost felt enchanted. It was as if he was reading, or rather seeing alive, the words of the ancient books of wisdom. He felt the same pain in his heart. He felt the same song in his heart.

"You, Brave One, you have loved me a long time. You have only met me today, but for many seasons you have written the beauty and the wisdom of my name into the alphabet of your life. No one who is not already acquainted with me can ever be introduced to me," said the dragon.

"But the people from my town say that my life is a strange life. If your name is in my life, then, with due respect, I suspect you have a strange name, sir?"

"My name will be strange only to those sad souls who live gray lives. But you have been familiar with it for a long time. And since times ancient, all those who were willing to be called by the dreaded name have known me."

The mystery was becoming deeper and deeper and The Owner of the House of Many Colors was sure that the dragon knew that he was at that very moment feeling more timid than all other timid souls had ever been. He was ready to excuse himself, or just turn around and run, when the deep, warm and dangerous voice invited and commanded him, "Come closer, Brave One."

He did not know whether it was because of fear to disobey, or courage to dare to go closer that he was able to approach the most frightening creature he had ever encountered. Standing right in front of the dragon, he noticed for the first time the golden chain around its neck and the beautiful name-plaque with the words:

Excellence, Dragon of Greatness, Friend of the Lowly Dragon Significance, and Opener of Palace Doors, Mighty Slayer of the Evil Ones, Mediocrity and Compromise.

Chapter 8

Of Small Words and Great Meanings

The heart is deceitful above all things, and desperately wicked: who can know it?

JEREMIAH 17:9

IT IS A very short word that will determine a great deal of what will happen to us in time without end. We may think that in eternity it would stand us in good stead to be able to give account of great endeavors, but this one short word could show all of our efforts that may have been so worthy in the eyes of others, to be nothing but insignificant. Meaningless efforts towards nothingness. Wasted time. Wasted dreams. Wasted life.

The little word that will prove to be the nemesis of many is of course the three-lettered word "why". For in the deep unseen part of the heart is the reality of who we really are.

The eyes of Him who sees beyond and within do not see appearances. They pierce through our successes, through our apparent humble service for our deserving causes, through the most worthy of our commitments. They see where no-one can see without His discerning assistance. When the accolades are forgotten, when the awards have lost their lustre and the admiration of crowds is no more, then only this little word will remain. Then the piercing eyes will reveal what they have beheld: the motive of the heart. Nothing but the *why* will matter.

I have little advice to give to those who wonder about the motives of their hearts, my struggle is with the motive of my own. Maybe we would do well to suspect the best motives in others and ruthlessly inspect our own hearts for falsity, vanity or vainglory. Maybe we will be wise to accept that the deep suspicion that we are not reaching the heights we are destined for, is founded in the *why* of our hearts. To underestimate the deceitfulness of the heart is to open it up to deceit. To know the susceptibility of one's own heart is to protect it. And when our steps begin to stray, it is in the heart we should look for reasons.

In the court-case of the stolen apple-pie, the fingers blamed the hands for moving them, the hands accused the arms, the arms blamed the eyes for looking at the forbidden food, the eyes blamed the neck for turning the head, the neck blamed the nose for smelling and the nose blamed the brain for planning the theft. The brain blamed the heart for allowing this state of affairs. And the heart was guilty.

As we watch where destiny led our hero, we see more and more of his heart. It is often true that the closer people get to reaching their dreams and realizing their visions, the more shadows of darkness begin to veil their hearts, but not so in this case. We discover the *why* in this noble heart and we see beauty. The beauty of a heart finding its destiny in its concern for the destiny of others. It seems that the great souls of history became great, without really being aware of it. Theirs was a journey away from the self and in this altruistic quest, they found meaning. Making a difference became a becoming.

Not so with the darkest souls of history. Starting out on the quest for meaning, most of them reached the joyous beginnings of a noble life, but sadly succumbed to the ingenious ploy of the Evil One to infect noble hearts with an infatuation with their own nobility. They became aware, not of the difference their lives could bring about, but of how different they had become.

Then they lost the very object of their infatuation, and they were noble no more. Only, they were oblivious of the fact.

Having started with an outward quest, they end up locked in the prison of self-obsession. Their lives become the lonely expression, not of becoming, but of unbecoming.

Our friend, as we shall see, was not of this kind. We, as he, can also desire the beauty of never losing sight of those around us. Seeing brokenness is the only way to become whole. Reaching outward brings inner beauty. Our hearts can be whole only as we allow them to be even fractionally as broken as the heart of the God we serve. This is the risk of love and the beauty of life.

To love at all is to be vulnerable. Love anything,
and your heart will certainly be wrung and possibly be broken.
If you want to make sure of keeping it intact, you must give
your heart to no one, not even an animal. Wrap it carefully
around with hobbies and little luxuries; avoid all entanglements;
lock it up safe in the casket – safe, dark, motionless, airless –
it will change. It will not be broken; it will become
unbreakable, impenetrable, irredeemable. The alternative
to tragedy, or at least to the risk of tragedy, is damnation.
The only place outside Heaven where you can be perfectly
safe from all the dangers and perturbations of love is Hell.
C. S. Lewis

If I do not have love, I am nothing.

1 CORINTHIANS 13:2 (NIV)

open doors and
thrones of destiny

O, MIGHTY DRAGON Excellence, Dragon Mediocrity has been a great danger to my people for a long time and to know that you have slain it is very good news to me," said The Owner of the House of Many Colors, thinking that Excellence had already slain the enemy of The Town called Potential.

"You do not understand. The evil Dragon Mediocrity and his friend Compromise are still alive and we do not have much time. We must leave immediately for the palace," said Dragon Excellence with a sense of urgency that made The Owner of the House of Many Colors shudder.

"But what about the key to the palace?" he asked, with the due respect reflecting in his voice.

"Fear not, Brave One, you have found the key already," said the dragon, and although the Brave One did not understand, he could not doubt a voice that spoke with so much authority.

With that, the mighty Dragon Excellence stood up and towered majestically over The Owner of the House of Many Colors, who at that moment discovered depths of fear and heights of admiration that he had only read about in the ancient books of wisdom. He thought he saw the mighty dragon smile. Before he knew what was happening to him, he was scooped up by the strong claw-like hands of the dragon and was looking down from his elevated position on the back of the dragon.

They exited the cave and the dragon spread his huge wings that looked like eagle-wings, only many times bigger, and then they soared. The Owner of the House of Many Colors was as high as he had so many times dreamed about before that day.

"Would you like to fly on your own?" the voice commanded even when asking.

"But I have no wings, Mister Dragon Excellence, sir," said The Owner of the House of Many Colors with as much respect as he could, hoping that the dragon would forsake the idea.

"You do not need wings, you need eyes that desire to see from on high. You need a soul that desires to understand the highest good. You need a heart that desires to conquer the highest evils and the deepest fears. You need ears that desire to hear the highest call. You do not need wings, dear friend, you already have them. Trust, O Brave One, trust," said Dragon Excellence in a playful way, but still with so much authority that The Owner of the House of Many Colors felt that this was far from being a game.

Could this be happening to him? He felt that this was the end, but he was strangely excited. He felt the surging gladness in his heart, as fear was being defeated by trust. And then he jumped towards his dream of flying.

Flying was easy that day. He felt the wind and he saw the world and it was beautiful. And all the while Excellence was near him and even the possibility of falling seemed preposterous.

They flew over The Town called Potential and The Owner of the House of Many Colors thought how sad it was that those almost wonderful, vaguely beautiful, very nearly ingenious and definitely (although not really aware of it) very precious people were all so afraid of high places.

After that, it was higher again towards the palace. It looked even bigger and more dignified and ancient than before. It seemed so long ago that he had left to go and search for the key. The key? In all the excitement he had completely forgotten about the key.

His flight ended with a rather undignified landing in front of the great palace and he was now standing in front of the door that was still locked and still looked as formidable as before. He remembered his suffering in trying to open it and looked around for the reassuring presence of Excellence, but the dragon was nowhere to be seen.

With a door still locked and without a key, he was just about to begin feeling despondent. What was he to do? He had been told by Dragon Excellence that he already had the key and here he was, without the very key he had been told he had. To be honest, he had no idea where it was. And where was the dragon that had been so insistent that they had to get to the palace as quickly as possible?

Suddenly, he heard something that sounded like singing. It reminded him of the beautiful, great and dangerous, warm voice of Dragon Excellence, but it also sounded very much like the voice within the gale. It seemed as if the words were coming from far away yet also from within his own heart. Then he recognized the words from *The Book of Separation – Comfort for Destined Purposes.*

As he was looking around him to find out where the voice had been coming from, The Owner of the House of Many Colors saw in front of him in the green grass a beautiful golden plaque. He immediately recognized it as the one that he had seen around the neck of the dragon.

He picked it up and then that which he was seeing and hearing became one thing. The words seemed to be alive and to become more present by the moment – written on the back of the plaque, lingering on the comfort of the breeze, whispering in the voice of his mind and echoing in the mountains as if constantly being sent from the heart of a great dragon. The Owner of the House of Many Colors joined in singing what was already all around and inside him and glowing from the golden name-plaque of Dragon Excellence:

Key of the Dreamer King - the Song of Perseverance

you dreamed and still the door was shut
keep on dreaming
you climbed, you bled
you tried
you shed your tears

and fought your fears
you dreamed but still the door was shut
keep on dreaming, climbing, bleeding, trying
shedding tears
and fighting fears
and then dream some more
for blood and dreams
unlock each door

He was still singing these beautiful words in a dreamy melody and looking at the golden plaque when suddenly he knew what he was holding in his hands ... "The key of the Dreamer King ..." He knew he had the key to the palace and that the moment of truth had come.

Once again The Owner of the House of Many Colors remembered the warning in ancient books of wisdom of the danger of unauthorised entry into palaces. He remembered a riddle called *Six to go, thereafter one, before the battle has been won*. The riddle in six parts ended with the warning:

Palaces of promise soon
can turn to palaces of doom.
If this here riddle you'll forget,
it will not be without regret.

He had always wondered if the time spent in learning the riddle by heart and also refreshing his memory often was really worth it, but standing in front of the palace with the key in his hands he certainly did not regret it. Trembling, he lifted the golden plaque and slid it into the keyhole of the palace door and effortlessly turned it.

The moment was one of awe. He pushed the majestic, ancient door and with here and there a dignified squeak, it slowly opened, but, disappointingly, he was not inside the palace yet. There was only another closed door behind it, as heavy as the first, but without a keyhole in it. There were six incomplete parts to a riddle written on the door. The Owner of the House of Many Colors immediately recognized them and never had he been more thankful for the ancient books of wisdom he had taken from the gray library.

He read out loud the first lines of the incomplete parts and then completed them. He knew that there would not be a second chance. With trembling voice he spoke to the closed doors. It felt as if completing the riddle took hours.

With every new rhyme, he felt the weight on his mind increasing. He was sure that he was not alone. As if in an arena and battling for life and death his mind and body were burning and shouting at him to run away and never return to this palace of doom. But he knew he had begun on a journey from which there was no return. He had to go through what felt like six eternal battles.

After completing each riddle he sensed victory, only to be drawn into battle again by the next. The six riddles are today still written on the palace door and it is said that all who wish to enter The Palace of Royalty Beyond and Within – Abode of their Majesties, Kings and Queens of Humanity from The Great City Potential still battle through them:

Of Choices:
The palace, bright colored, is surely not gray,
but why be abnormal now, what do you say?
So many are on the majority way,
why not be part of the sensible they?

Narrow the mind and broad is the way,
the middle of the road is deadly and gray.
Narrow the way that few ever find,
narrow the way, but broad is the mind.

Of Perseverance:
The quest, the quest, eternal quest.
Surely, now, surely, you do need a rest.

It matters not how far I've come,

too soon the stop, in vain the run.
Halfway is a luke-warm name,
Regret is hell's eternal flame.

Of Loyalty:
Forget the weak, forget the lost,
those who stray must pay the cost.

Forget the broken? Scorn the poor? Forget the humble, close
my door?
Then who will come, then who will care? I'm broken too and
need repair.
The dignity of broken kind, is never seen by selfish blind.

Of Love:
The pain, the tears, why risk the heart?

It's true: no risk, no pain, no dart,
but neither love, nor life, nor heart.

Of Fear:
I feel your presence, o mighty lord, Fear.
A friend or a foe, I pray thee, who's near?

Know and face and conquer me,
then looking back, a friend I've been.

Befriend and learn to live with me,
I'll be a deadly enemy.

Of Death:
My name is Death, why don't you flee?
Who dares to face a foe like me?

O, Death, once fierce, once strong and tall,
I've lived in full, you seem so small.

There was nothing left to do, nothing left to say. Then the long silence of expectation was broken as the door slowly opened as if inviting its visitor in to the most wonderful place he had ever seen.

There was splendor beyond description. Countless thrones of gold filled a throne room so spacious and colorful, that The Owner of the House of Many Colors immediately decided on repainting and expanding his house, as soon as he returned home.

For a while he was overcome at the sight of such beauty and splendor, and then, true to the way he had always been keenly interested to discover new things, new wisdom and new beauty, he began his exploration of The Palace of Royalty Beyond and Within – Abode of their Majesties, Kings and Queens of Humanity from The Great City Potential.

The sun was playing through the open door and dancing on the thrones of gold. There seemed to be an inscription on each throne. He went closer and saw that every throne was inscribed with ancient letters that he had only seen in the ancient books in his library.

As he started reading what was written on each throne, he understood more than ever before that the people of The Town called Potential were meant to be wonderful, beautiful, and ingenious and were definitely very precious, if only they could realize it. He understood that day what their true potential was.

The Owner of the House of Many Colors knew that he had not only found his own destiny, but the destiny of The Town called Potential.

Inscribed on the thrones were names. Yes, on every throne, in beautiful ancient writing, he could read a familiar name. And every name had an added title. In amazement and wonder he read aloud names such as:

Aldore from the Nethergreen –
King of Greatnewness
Olmardena from Brightstreams –
Queen of Bravejoy
Asterbrontt from Oversky –
King of Highdreams
Delgralina from Farview –

Queen of Everlove
Gomerthall from Deepstrength –
King of Longbattle
Brendorkann from Highcrest –
King of Neverfear
Gwandelinta from Valley Selfless –
Queen of Truebeauty

Oh, he had to tell them. They had to know who they were really meant to be. They had to know of their beautiful palace of many colors. They had to know of the great Dragon Excellence. They had to hear the words from the Song of Perseverance. And, more than anything, they had to know what their names were. They had to know their destiny.

And then he read his own name, written on a throne of gold. As he was reading it, it was burning inside him. He was not just The Strange One, The Owner of the House of Many Colors. His name was indeed what he had always known it to be. In ancient letters the true meaning of his name was explained, yet it was still hard for him to understand. Everything was beginning to seem more and more mysterious to him. Even so, as was the case with all the other names, it was clearly written that he was a king. And he believed.

Chapter 9

Of Endings and Beginnings

You have made my days a mere handbreadth; the span of my years is as nothing before you. Each man's life is but a breath. Man is a mere phantom as he goes to and fro: He bustles about, but only in vain; he heaps up wealth, not knowing who will get it. "But now, Lord, my hope is in you."

PSALM 39:5-7 (NIV)

Death is swallowed up in victory. O death, where is thy sting? O grave, where is thy victory?

1 CORINTHIANS 15:54-55

L ET US, SINCE we are approaching the end of the book, consider the end of time.

We have considered earlier in the book how many pilgrims have lost their way in the morasses of suffering. Ideas and illusions that life should be easy and that turning to God would eliminate suffering from their lives have been the main cause of their disillusionment. Life is not easy. Suffering is real. And easy explanations for our struggles cause them to be more intense and our understanding of them more confused. Yet, suffering, complex as the questions it brings about may be, is not without meaning.

Arguably, the epitome of suffering is experienced in the agonies of death – mourning the death of loved ones, young and old; or living with the constant knowledge, consciously or subconsciously, that death may be at our doorstep, even this very day. Can we still, honestly, even in the frightening shadows of the valley of death where we live every day of our lives, confess that we see purpose in this brief sojourn on a suffering planet?

We do not have many options: We can believe that life does not make sense, has no author or director, and ends in death, beyond which there is nothing. Paul concludes that all that is left for those with this hopeless, futureless, temporary view of life and death is to "eat and drink, for tomorrow we die." (cf. 1 Corinthians 15:32).

This is the cynical perspective of the famous French philosopher, Jean-Paul Sartre. His conclusion is simply that, "Every existing thing is born without reason, prolongs itself out of weakness and dies by chance." Centuries earlier, Voltaire also found no meaning in life or death, and his conclusion does not help us either: "Life is a bad joke," he says.

We get even more lost as we listen to André Maurois, of the same cynical and hopeless circle:

> The universe is indifferent. Who created it?
> Why are we here on this puny mudheap spinning
> in infinite space? I have not the slightest idea,
> and I am quite convinced that no one has the least idea.

When we go to the eastern philosophies, the flickering of the candle of hope is very brief. Yes, they tell us, there is a future; with the right karma we can escape the miseries and suffering of life and death. Yet, as we look around us, we have to conclude that there is no escape. If we are to be reincarnated until we have become the devout creatures worthy of escaping the endless circle of suffering, who will make it? Even the holiest, most spiritual or karmically progressed seem to be unable to escape the "bad joke."

No, we are not helped. Whereas cynicism leads us

to a black hole of nothingness with no eternity, eastern philosophies trap us in an eternity of endless cycles of self-improvement which no-one seems to have perfected through centuries of fastings, meditations, and reincarnations.

We would be wise to turn to Him who said,

I am the resurrection, and the life: he that believeth in me, though he were dead, yet shall he live: And whosoever liveth and believeth in me shall never die. Believest thou this?

JOHN 11:25-26

Living with this promise, we can experience its becoming more and more of a reality as our lives become more like His. Christ prepares us for death in the future by helping us to be ready for it in the present. The ancient people lived with a very prominent conciousness of death and readiness for it. Modern spirituality has lost this emphasis. Consider the advice of three of the giants from the past:

"You cannot pass a day devoutly unless you think of it as your last. (It is) the most essential of all works ... The man who lives daily with the thought of death is to be admired, and the man who gives himself to it by the hour is a saint."

Climacus

"We cannot greatly deplore the blindness of men
who do not want to think of death, and who turn away
from an inevitable thing which we could be happy
to think of often. Death only troubles carnal people."
Francios Fénelon

"Happy is he who always hath the hour of death
before his eyes, and daily prepareth himself to die ...
When it is morning, think thou mayest die before night;
and when evening comes, dare not to promise thyself
the next morning. Be thou therefore always in a readiness,
and so lead thy life that death may never take thee unprepared."
Thomas à Kempis

Preparation for death takes place as we learn to die daily, and in many ways. There is no other way to live, than to die daily; there is no other way to die, than to have died many times before the day of death.

And so, we turn to the last chapter of our story and find again our hero who could not be overcome by even the most dangerous challenges of life. If we live this way, we will discover the secret of life.

from gray, square houses to palaces of many colors

MAKING HIS WAY down the mountain, The Owner of the House of Many Colors had only one thing in mind and that was to let all the people of The Town called Potential know about The Palace of Royalty Beyond and Within – Abode of their Majesties, Kings and Queens of Humanity from The Great City Potential.

He was so amazed about all the things that had happened to him, that the thought of Dragon Mediocrity did not even once cross his mind. He took the golden Key of the Dreamer King with him because he knew that it would take some convincing before the people living in their gray, square houses would believe that they were meant to be kings and queens. He had to have some evidence, if he was ever going to convince them of flying dragons, not to mention flying owners of colored houses!

The Town called Potential looked even more gray and dull and the sadness of it all was overwhelming to The Owner of the House of Many Colors. There were no children playing in the streets, for fear of the evil Dragon Mediocrity. (There was by now no doubt that Mediocrity was the nightly, and lately almost daily, man-eating visitor.)

The first thing that The Owner of the House of Many Colors did was to go to his own house. It was easy to get his family to believe that they were destined, not for The Town called Potential, but for The Great City Potential, especially when they heard that the palace was not a square gray palace, but a palace of many colors, not unlike their house of many colors, only much bigger and brighter.

To them it was almost the natural thing to believe that they should go and live in the palace, since they had, as it were, a picture of a palace in their minds ever since they could remember. Having lived with such a palace mentality for so long, it was easy to believe that there was, in fact, an actual palace.

And so The Owner of the House of Many Colors and his family set out to convince the people who were all hiding in their gray, square houses to gather in the town hall.

It was not a difficault task to get the people to meet in the town hall. Word was spread that it concerned the safety, security and stability of each citizen and this was enough to get the attention of everyone. Soon the town hall was packed to capacity.

But the meeting was not a great success. The Owner of the House of Many Colors gave account of his experiences in the mountain. The people listened as if under a spell. Hearing of the kind Dragon Excellence gave them hope for deliverance from Mediocrity.

The Owner of the House of Many Colors saw the magic of destiny in their eyes as he was telling them of their names written on the thrones in The Palace of Royalty Beyond and Within – Abode of their Majesties, Kings and Queens of Humanity from The Great City Potential.

But when he proposed that they pack up and leave

with him to the Great City Potential, he saw the fear return to their eyes, the deadly poison of their life-long imprisonment within the boundary walls of safety, security and stability.

No matter how he explained that they were one journey away from a life they could never have imagined, they could think of only one thing, the deadly attacks of Dragon Mediocrity. He pleaded with them, but the spark of hope he had seen in their eyes moments before had gone and one by one they left for the cold safety of their gray houses. The gray of the evening slowly turned into the black of a hopeless night.

In the dark of the night The Owner of the House of Many Colors realized that there was no other way – Mediocrity had to be killed before the people of The Town called Potential would ever be palace-dwellers. He knew he had to go back up the mountain. His family wanted to go with him, but he told them to stay behind. They were needed in town.

The town was full of people paralyzed by fear and they would need the few who still had hope and courage. Without the presence of these brave souls, all those almost wonderful, vaguely beautiful, very nearly ingenious and definitely (although not really aware of it) very precious people would be left at the mercy of Mediocrity and their fears. And both the dragon and their fears were deadly enemies.

As he was leaving The Town called Potential very early the next morning, he could sense that even the air was filled with the weight of what was at stake. Hope and fear were heading for a final battle. The mountain lay in front of him and he was not sure if it would finally prove to be Mount Royal or indeed Mount Impossiblility. Would this mountain become part of the Great Desert Despair or was there still hope? With these thoughts he headed up the mountain.

He knew that if there was to be any hope, he would have to find the mighty Dragon Excellence. Mediocrity had to die. He was even thinking that he would fight Mediocrity himself, but this thought was based not only on the fact that The Owner of the House of Many Colors had one of the bravest hearts of all people in ancient times, but also on the fact that he had never seen Mediocrity after it had been banned from The Town called Potential.

Even with the knowledge of the ancient books of wisdom, he could never have imagined how evil and deadly Mediocrity had become. He would soon find out that, even though his heart was brave enough to fight any evil dragon when necessary, bravery alone would not be enough.

When The Owner of the House of Many Colors

reached the middle regions of Mount Possibility, he heard the frightening sound of a dragon's breathing. He knew from the evil and ominous atmosphere filling the air, that it could not be the mighty Dragon Excellence. In his encounters with Dragon Excellence he always had the urge to flee, (and presently he definitely wanted to flee) but he always also had the desire to embrace (and presently he definitely felt far from wanting to embrace). Utter revulsion and a deep sense of evil filled his being.

As he glanced at Mediocrity through the thick bush between him and the dragon, he saw what was to him the most loathsome creature he had ever seen. He could see the cruel, selfish and indulging look in Mediocrity's eyes. He could smell the stench of his breath and of his body and he could see the filth and the mess that Mediocrity had created on that part of the mountain.

Nobody who had known the dragon when it was still a cute baby dragon would ever have imagined that it would one day become such a gigantic, evil and dangerous brute.

The Owner of the House of Many Colors had never encountered anything as revolting. He knew he was in the presence of the worst enemy of The Town called Potential. He knew this enemy had to be destroyed. He also knew, staring at the colossal monster, that no man had the strength within himself to destroy Mediocrity without any help. He knew that he had to find that other wonderfully frightening dragon, the mighty Dragon Excellence.

Carefully he moved away and started out on his journey towards The Palace of Royalty Beyond and Within – Abode of their Majesties, Kings and Queens of Humanity from The Great City Potential.

"I've been waiting for you," he heard the familiar voice, hours later, just as he was entering the beautiful gardens of the palace. Although he was still awe-struck at the deep sound of danger, his heart lit up with hope and joy.

"O mighty Dragon Excellence, I've seen the enemy of my people. He is gigantic and evil and by now he may have eaten even more of the precious people of The Town called Potential. Mister Dragon, sir, you have to help us!"

"I have seen him too, Brave One."

The deep voice was sad.

"I have seen his strength and it is great. I will not be able to help you."

"I don't understand, mighty Excellence. I have here with me your name written in gold: Excellence, Dragon of Greatness, Friend of the Lowly Dragon Significance, and Opener of Palace Doors, Mighty Slayer of the Evil Ones, Mediocrity and Compromise. I respectfully ask whether you have forgotten who you are, Sir?"

"I know who I am, Brave One, but have you not read in the ancient books that the strength of a dragon increases greatly once he has eaten human flesh? Dragon Mediocrity and Dragon Compromise have within them the strength of many and have become very mighty dragons."

"But you are the mighty slayer," came the desperate reply of The Owner of the House of Many Colors.

"Even I will need new strength before I would be able to conquer Mediocrity and Compromise now that they have eaten human flesh," said Excellence.

"But what can we do?" By now The Owner of the House of Many Colors sounded very desperate.

Strangely calm, but also deeply sad, the dragon answered, "You can go and fetch your family and come and live here in the palace. In these higher regions of Mount Royal you will be safe. The air on high mountains is too thin and clean for evil dragons."

Then, hesitantly, and with a big dragon tear rolling down his cheek, he added, "Or there is an alternative, dear Brave One."

"If the alternative will help us kill the evil dragons, then we have no other choice. There are too many almost wonderful, vaguely beautiful, very nearly ingenious and definitely (although not really aware of it) very precious people in The Town called Potential who will have to die if we don't choose the alternative," said The Owner of the House of Many Colors, ready for action and positive that he and Dragon Excellence would be able to kill Mediocrity and Compromise.

And then, as an afterthought to his readiness for whatever the alternative was, he added, "And what is this alternative, O mighty Excellence?"

There was a long moment of silence. The big dragon put his giant claw tenderly on the shoulder of The Owner of the House of Many Colors. "I will have to get food that will increase my strength to more than that of the evil dragons, Brave One."

In his usual optimistic way, The Owner of the House of Many Colors tried to reassure Dragon Excellence that food was not a problem. "Just tell me where to go and I will bring you any food you need. I will travel anywhere, I am not afraid of mountains or oceans, dangers or obstacles. You will have the food you need, O mighty Excellence."

His voice, trembling and filled with agony, the dragon answered his believing friend, "The only food that would give me enough strength is the heart of a brave man, the flesh of a fearless lover of life, the head of a man of great dreams, the legs of a conqueror of high mountains and the hands of him who has paged through ancient books of wisdom and has reached out to touch beautiful things."

Suddenly, The Owner of the House of Many Colors was cold with fear. Looking into those dangerously wild and loving eyes, filled with sadness, he remembered the words Excellence had spoken to him before, "Fear can be the good thing that makes you a hero, or the bad thing that makes you a coward ... "

As if the dragon could read his thoughts, he said, "You are a Brave One, no matter what you decide, you could never be a coward. If you should wish to go and fetch your family and come and live in the palace, you may do so."

The Owner of the House of Many Colors looked down into the valley. He saw the sad, gray, square houses. He thought of how all the children would never grow up to see the things that he had seen.

He thought of how not one of them would ever see the world from the top of Mount Possibility. He remembered what it was like to fly. He looked again at the great colorful palace and knew they would never set eyes on it. He thought of the stench of the revolting breath of Mediocrity and imagined how those filthy teeth would sink into the flesh of all those potential kings and queens of Humanity, without any one of them ever tasting the joy of ruling and living in The Great City Potential. He thought of the beautiful names that were written on the golden thrones.

Aldore from the Nethergreen - King of Greatnewness would die as Plain old Al, Olmardena from Brightstreams - Queen of Bravejoy would die as Good old Olma. Every potential king and queen of Humanity would die as a slave to Mediocrity. Die without ever becoming what they were meant to be. Die without ever having lived.

The Owner of the House of Many Colors thought of all the beautiful names in the throne room of the palace, and then he remembered his own name. He looked at the palace and wanted so much to become a king, but he knew at that moment that the only thing that could make him the king that he was destined to be, was to choose not to become a king at all.

For the first time he understood the mystery. He understood the true meaning of his name. And he understood his destiny.

He remembered the words from the ancient book of wisdom, "One Life, One Death," and these words of wisdom helped him make the most important decision of his life:

Only he who is ready to die, can truly live, but he who considers himself ready only for life, not death, does not know that he is, in fact, already dead and has never really been alive.

"I am ready," he said, and the sad, sad dragon knew that the voice was that of a man who would not be persuaded.

"I knew that you were ready the moment I first saw you, Brave One. Be strong."

The last moments of The Owner of the House of Many Colors were mysterious moments indeed. The scene was gruesome, yet sublime – speaking of both agony and ecstasy.

Suffering and joy were never in such perfect harmony as on that day, the day when The Owner of the House of Many Colors gave his life away …

Ancient history records the fight between Excellence and the two friends Mediocrity and Compromise also as a very mysterious event. It is written that after Excellence had received unimaginable strength from eating the flesh of a mighty man of valor, he went on to destroy the two vile dragons. Not once could any one of the two evil dragons put even as much as a dirty claw on the mighty dragon Excellence. However, the ancient records show that it took days before the two dragons would finally give their last breath. It is said that no dragon had ever died as unwillingly and slowly as the evil dragons

Mediocrity and Compromise.

The screams of agony and evil curses could be heard many miles from the scene. In The Town called Potential all the people came running out of their gray square houses when the screaming had stopped and a rumbling sound could be heard. What they saw were the dead bodies of the two evil dragons tumbling down the mountain.

From the mountain came a voice from which they wanted to flee, but it was too irresistible. It was the voice of Excellence. And of course certain Strange Ones were the first to start packing and to move to higher ground. It was not long until all the people from The Town called Potential were high mountain dwellers, living in The Palace of Royalty Beyond and Within – Abode of their Majesties, Kings and Queens of Humanity from The Great City Potential.

Soon all the houses in The Town called Potential were used by pig farmers as pigsties, except of course a certain house of many colors. The pig farmers moved into that house and lived like kings. The house was still fully furnished and everywhere inside there were beautiful works of art. They did, however, find it strange that on the door of one very large room these words were written: "The Room of Ancient Wisdom," but there were only empty shelves in that room.

And on Mount Royal, in that ancient palace of many

colors, great and noble kings and queens would dwell for centuries. The names on the thrones would constantly change as old kings and queens died and new ones ascended to their thrones. There was just one throne, the one in the centre of the throne room, the one full of the most precious and colorful stones, that remained empty.

Through the centuries, no one ever changed the name inscribed on that throne. Princes and princesses were being brought up to be like the hero whose name was written on the throne of many colors. At their coronation, they had to take "The Oath for Living a Life of Many Colors." One can still find the words of this oath in the ancient book, *Guidelines for Palace Living*:

I, as aspiring member of the Royal Family of The Great City Potential, do solemnly swear that in the one life that I have to live:

- I will be an artist of life and fight all enemies tempting me to mundane living.
- I will always be a bidder at the Auctions of the Libraries of Wisdom.
- I will never entertain little dragons, however cute they may be.
- I will be a palace-finder and never dwell in the gray houses of conformity.

- I will choose the mountain peaks of challenge and not the valleys of security.
- I will not be found in the company of the ruling dragons: Pride, Covetousness and Lust, nor underestimate the dragons: Ease, Procrastination, Fear, Grudge, Half-Truth, Know-All and Two-Face.
- I will not fall victim to Mediocrity or Compromise.
- I will live with a mission, in reaching out will be my becoming.

Before the final statement of the oath, the most solemn moment of the coronation arrived. There would be an hour of silence as the new king or queen would have the only opportunity in a lifetime to be seated on the throne of many colors. In the presence of all the inhabitants of The Great City Potential, the Vow of Excellence was made. A life of royalty would begin with the slow, irrevocable vow:

- I will pay the price.

For all ages to follow, in all of that great city, the name on the empty throne was spoken with a hush, yet longed for with passion, embraced without restraint. It became the adopted name of every king and queen.

It is believed that the Great City Potential can still today be found in Mount Possiblility. Rumor has it that many citizens from the Country Dreamless have heard of this great city.

Many have come, reporting journeys to the edge of suffering and endurance. It is said that the country Humanity has grown because of the journeys of these travelers from far-away places in that country called Dreamless, places like the cities Majority, Security and Tragedy and The Great Desert Despair.

And they are all told of the extraordinary life of an ordinary man. He lived a life of beauty and meaning. They are told of the dark times during all those years when men did not understand the meaning of his name, not because it came from an unknown ancient tongue, but because it spoke of a way of life too difficult for gray house dwellers in love with Mediocrity.

But now the citizens of The Great City Potential understand the meaning of that name and it is to them both beautiful and awesome. And they know that without that which that name stood for, they would accomplish nothing, even their own names would have no meaning as life would indeed have no meaning.

Is there any endeavor, any cause, any destiny or purpose worth anything? Look deeply, and you will find this name at the heart of it.

His name was Sacrifice.

In self-giving, if anywhere, we touch a rhythm
not only of all creation but of all being. For
the Eternal Word also gives Himself in sacrifice;
and not only on Calvary ... From before the foundation
of the world He surrenders begotten Deity
back to begetting Deity in obedience ... From the highest
to the lowest, self exists to be abdicated and, by that abdication,
becomes the more truly self, to be thereupon yet more
abdicated, and so forever ... What is outside the system of self-
giving is not earth, nor nature, nor ordinary life, but simply
and solely Hell ... That fierce imprisonment in the self is but
the obverse of the self-giving which is absolute reality.
C. S. Lewis